SAMPSON TECHNICAL INSTITUTE

NORTH CAROLINA
STATE
DEPT. O
LIBRARIES

S0-BIN-737

2/74

DEPT. OF COMMUNITY COLLEGES
BOARD OF EDUCATION)
DEPT. OF EDUCATION)

# THE WANKEL RC ENGINE

TJ
790
A5
1969

# The Wankel RC Engine

## DESIGN AND PERFORMANCE

**R. F. Ansdale,** C.Eng., M.I.Mech.E., M.S.A.E.

with a special contribution by **D. J. Lockley,** M.Sc.

SOUTH BRUNSWICK AND NEW YORK:
A. S. BARNES AND COMPANY

Library
Sampson Technical Institute

First American edition 1969
A. S. Barnes & Co., Inc.
Cranbury, N.J. 08512

Library of Congress Catalog Card Number 69–18692

498  07410  2

© R. F. Ansdale 1968

Filmset by Photoprint Plates Ltd.
Wickford, Essex and printed in England by
Butler & Tanner Ltd., Frome, Somerset

# CONTENTS

ALTHOUGH THE AUTHOR IS SOLELY RESPONSIBLE FOR OPINIONS, statements and conclusions contained in this book about the NSU/Wankel RC engine, it is obvious that he would have been unable to acquire the necessary familiarity with the subject matter without the most valuable advice and assistance of individuals and companies concerned with the development of the Wankel RC engine concept.

In particular, thanks are due to Felix Wankel, the inventor, and to Dr. G. S. von Heydekampf, the Managing Director of NSU Motorenwerke A.G., for facilitating so comprehensive a study of this engine, reaching back to the very first news of this RC engine stirring the engineering world. Nor is less appreciation due to Dr. Ing. Walter Froede, Dipl.Ing. H.D. Paschke and their associates for their competent and patient explanations of technical intricacies and performance phenomena peculiar to this type of engine.

Although not all licensees were equally prepared to assist with guidance and information, Messrs. Fichtel & Sachs A.G., The Curtiss-Wright Corporation, Toyo Kogyo Co., Ltd., and Yanmar Diesel Engine Co., Ltd., were most helpful.

Mr. K. Yamamoto, who heads the Rotary Engine Development Division at Toyo Kogyo in Hiroshima, provided illuminating particulars and illustrations about the work which is in progress under his guidance. Mr. J. E. Lonsdale and Mr. B. P. Ryle worked patiently through the draft manuscript and made very constructive suggestions for clarifying and improving the text. Mr. Gerald G. Summerville also gave very helpful advice with regard to some of the mathematical problems.

Appreciation is expressed to the following Companies and Organisations for permission to quote from their publications and for their advice and assistance:

The B.S.A. Group Research Centre, for permission to include various calculations which were made for a particular design study, and especially to Mr. D. J. Lockley, M.Sc., for his contribution to the mathematical appendix of this book. The Pontiac Motor Division of G.M.C. for supplying the excellent illustrations of their O.H.C. six cylinder Tempest engine. The British Petroleum Company Ltd., The Institution of Mechanical

Engineers and the Society of Automotive Engineers for permission to quote from various publications. The Champion Spark Plug Co., and Robert Bosch A.G., were particularly helpful with advice about ignition systems and spark plugs.

R. F. Ansdale.

# I

# Introduction to the NSU/ Wankel RC Engine, its Design and performance Characteristics

The modern automobile engine has enjoyed 90 years of continuous development dating back to 1878, when the German engineer, Dr. Nicholas August Otto, exhibited his first four-cycle engine, which he had invented in 1876, barely two years previously. The notion was originally conceived in 1862 by the Frenchman Alphonse, Beau de Rochas, at a time when most others preoccupied with internal combustion engine development, were fascinated by the Lenoir-cycle which, unlike the Otto-cycle, did not incorporate a compression phase.

Today it is preferable to use the term Otto-cycle rather than four-stroke cycle, as the latter is irrevocably linked with the reciprocating motion of conventional piston engines. To avoid any further confusion it is intended to use exclusively the expression 'Otto-cycle' and refer to its four constituent parts as phases, namely: induction phase, compression phase, expansion or working phase and finally the exhaust phase. It may perhaps be reiterated that work is done exclusively over the entire expansion phase and part of the energy converted during this phase is subsequently required to overcome friction and resistances encountered during the other three phases. In practice port opening periods overlap and combustion as well as other phases may, in fact, commence before the conclusion of the preceding phase. This overlapping of phases occurs in reciprocating engines, and is an essential part of the design. The significance of such overlapping is not necessarily the same in rotary and reciprocating engine working cycles.

It is most interesting to note that the quest for positive displacement rotary piston machines dates back several centuries and actually pre-dates the invention of the reciprocating piston principle which posed problems far more amenable to the actual and theoretical assessment of engineers and inventors who were contemporaries of James Watt, and concerned themselves with rotary piston pumps or engines.

Nevertheless, it would be wrong to assume that the reciprocating piston, connecting rod and crank idea was at once universally acclaimed. It was believed at the time that a considerable amount of energy was irrevocably lost when the great masses, associated with the then fashionable beam as part of the mechanism for converting reciprocating into rotary motion, were repeatedly stopped and then accelerated again. The idea of the indestructibility of energy had not caught on, or the virtues of the flywheel would have been more fully appreciated. In short, the piston, connecting rod and crank arrangement did not establish itself overnight. Indeed, considerable simultaneous efforts were being devoted to the development of direct acting rotary engines which did not require any means for the conversion of linear to rotary motion. James Watt himself, and his associate Murdock, also sought purely rotary solutions.

Early windmills and water wheels were probably the first rotary machines, although they undoubtedly converted the linear velocity of wind and water into rotary motion and power. A bewildering variety of possible rotary engine configurations seems to have attracted and, at the same time, confused inventive minds, thereby preventing the early success of purely rotary engines. Engineers and inventors appear to have believed that the shortcomings and problems encountered during the development of their rotary piston engines were perhaps due to errors of conception, hence they sought solutions in new and different configurations rather than overcome the specific problems confronting them. It would appear that inventive ingenuity at that time lacked the discipline now considered essential for successful research work. Possibly insufficient cumulative background knowledge and experience were available to facilitate a more rational approach which is now deemed indispensible. Unfortunately, it became easy, even fashionable, to heap ridicule on attempts to evolve purely rotary prime movers by pointing to the impressive and rapid advances in the reciprocating piston engine field. The failure to differentiate between fundamental design principles of rotary piston engines – including Prof. F. Reuleaux's[1] (1875) notable attempt, contained in his books – further complicated the issues without halting the quest for purely rotary engines.

It is certainly beyond the scope of this introduction to show the full extent of the rotary piston machine field, although it is important that those engaged in it obtain a realistic perspective. To begin with there were no means available which allowed a sensible separation of basic principles from mere mechanical problems peculiar to any specific design, and this made it easy to regard any inventor of a rotary piston engine with reserve and suspicion – even Prof. Reuleaux thought it necessary to disclaim that his classifications concerned rotary piston engines. An earlier appreciation of the true facts may have produced a different attitude, and thereby contributed to making the rotary piston engine story an earlier success. It was not until Felix Wankel finally mustered sufficient patience and energy to work through vast numbers of designs and inventions that a sensible classification emerged.[2] By arranging rotary piston machines according to various functional characteristics Wankel provided a truly comprehensive perspective of this whole intricate subject, which shows most useful shortcuts and a practical approach to the problems of positive displacement rotary piston prime movers.

About 2,000 specifications of rotary piston machines were filed by 1910 according to Barker[3].

Wankel's classification divides all possible configurations into four groups, as follows:

Rotary Piston Machines = 1. Single Rotation Machines (SIM).
( = ROPIMA)          2. Planetary Rotation Machines (PLM).
                    3. Rotating Piston Machines similar to SIM (SROM).
                    4. Rotating Piston Machines similar to PLM (PROM).

Note: Rotating Piston Machines are abbreviated ROM, are symbolised in groups 3 and 4 and must not be confused with Rotary Piston Machines (ROPIMA) which is the generic term for the whole family of machines.

Furthermore, as shown on the four classification charts in his book, Wankel distinguishes between the disposition and relative attitude of the axes of rotation, the motion of the components which contain variable chambers and their mode of engagement (meshing) whereby these variable volume chambers are formed. The charts show a possible total of no less than 864 different basic configurations, each one represented by a square showing a diagrammatic sketch when the design had been found and analysed. Further analysis revealed 278 configurations as decidedly impracticable and 149 have already been fully analysed and classified, leaving 437 basic configurations to be evaluated or invented. Moreover, every basic configuration may be executed in almost countless different ways, so that the classification charts are supplemented by model sheets, one for each square, on which individual design variations, etc. may be recorded for easy reference purposes.

The classification is somewhat similar to those of the species or of chemical elements, and like these, facilitates the prediction of characteristics and fundamental features of yet unknown designs. In short, Wankel's classification is a useful tool made available to research engineers and others who may become involved in rotary piston machine design or development. A great deal of time and money may be saved by providing these rapid references to the nearest related designs, and at the same time, it facilitates a quicker appraisal, as attention is drawn to essential features.

The classification does not differentiate between configurations upon a qualitative basis, as for instance the desirability of constant angular velocity of all rotating parts, nor does it show which configuration is capable of accommodating a sensible thermodynamic cycle. Wankel's classification deals with rotary piston machines in general, including pumps, compressors and engines; therefore the apparent omissions point to indispensible factors which make possible the conversion of a mere rotary piston machine into a ROTARY PISTON (RC) ENGINE (RC = Rotary Combustion). Some of these additional requirements are:

1. Port areas and all aspects of port timing must be such that efficient working cycles are possible. Cross-sectional areas of ports must control gas speeds within efficient design limits.
2. It must be possible to accommodate sensible gas sealing systems.
3. Adequate cooling must be possible.
4. The engine must not be larger, heavier or more costly to produce than reciprocating engines developing the same power.

5. Power output and fuel consumption should at least approach figures which the best reciprocating piston engines can attain and a rotary design should be capable of substantially exceeding the performance of the equivalent reciprocating piston engine in at least one of the factors of comparison, and preferably in more. In particular it should show considerable advantages in weight and space requirements for a given power output and the potential power output of the rotary piston engine ought to be greater than that of the conventional piston engine.

Undoubtedly other important requirements may or ought to be added to this exacting list, but it is not intended to provide a guide to rotary piston engine design in general. The purpose of this book is to show a practical approach to the design of the NSU/Wankel engine and discuss some of the phenomena encountered during the development of this new engine.

A great deal of the material here included is based upon already published data and information obtained from companies and individuals actively engaged upon the development of the NSU/Wankel type engine.

Familiarity with the intricacies of internal combustion engines is assumed, nevertheless it may be necessary to elaborate upon various characteristics in order to underline their significance with regard to rotary piston engines or explain why it was found expedient to rely upon different criteria.

REFERENCES
1. REULEAUX, F., *Theoretische Kinematic*, Macmillan, (1876).
2. WANKEL, F., *Rotary Piston Machines*, Iliffe Books Ltd., London, (1965).
3. BARKER, 'Mills to Turbines', *Engineer*, January 13th, (1939).

# 2

# The Essentials of Rotary Piston Internal Combustion Engines

Before elaborating essential features of rotary piston engines it may be opportune to recall that *any heat engine is a mechanism capable of converting the potential heat energy contained in the fuel supplied into measurable mechanical work.* Furthermore, it may be reiterated that according to the first law of thermodynamics energy can neither be created nor destroyed. It must, therefore, be true that the energy supplied – in the form of fuel, i.e. in thermal units/lb., of fuel – is equal to the energy converted into mechanical work plus heat rejected with the exhaust gases plus heat lost to coolants and the environment. Ideally, all the potential heat energy ought to be converted into mechanical work; unfortunately this is impossible as friction must be overcome. Heat is lost by radiation and indispensible auxiliaries such as the oil pump, generator, fan and water pump must be driven and, therefore, require power. Consequently it is necessary to differentiate between the thermal efficiency (the relationship between the heat converted and the heat supplied) and brake thermal efficiency, that is the energy available to do external work. If anything, RC engine designs, for example the NSU/Wankel, are better off in this respect as they are essentially low friction engines, the number of their moving parts being small (Fig. 2.1), and the forces on their contact areas, where relative motion occurs, are also modest. Further gains are possible if the auxiliaries, equally indispensible for both types of engines, are specifically designed for RC engines and not simply inherited from reciprocating engine practice.

Indicated horsepower (i.h.p.) may be defined as the work done by the gases on the piston and brake horsepower (b.h.p.) as the measurable work transmitted by the crankshaft.

The efficiency of any mechanism is $\dfrac{\text{output power}}{\text{input power}}$ which may be re-written for combustion engines as efficiency $= \dfrac{\text{b.h.p.}}{\text{i.h.p.}} = \dfrac{\text{i.h.p.} - \text{f.h.p.}}{\text{i.h.p.}}$ where f.h.p. is friction horsepower

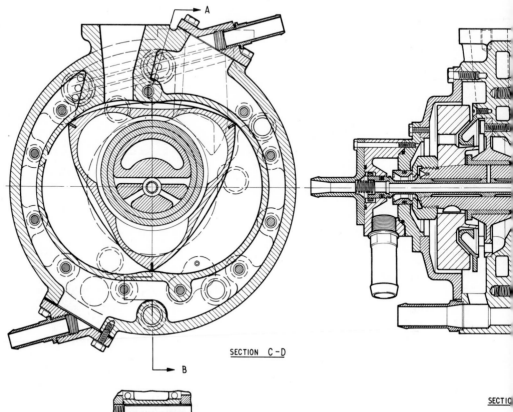

SECTION C-D

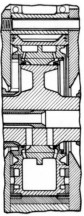

PART SECTION A-B

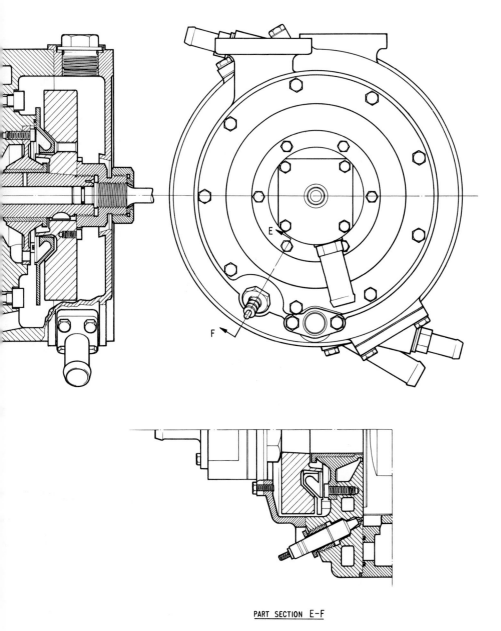

PART SECTION E-F

Fig. 2.1. Although Dr. Ing. W. Froede's inversion of the SIM type engine into a PLM resulted in a considerable simplification, the design still looks rather complex especially in comparison with the latest types of engine. See Plate 5.1

and any other mechanical losses which occur. The thermal efficiency of an engine may be based on i.h.p. or b.h.p. figures which means that

$$\text{indicated thermal efficiency} = \frac{\text{heat equivalent of i.h.p.}}{\text{heat content of fuel supplied}}$$

$$= \frac{\text{i.h.p.} \times 42\cdot416}{\text{lb/min of fuel} \times \text{calorific value}}.$$

$$\text{brake thermal efficiency} = \frac{\text{heat equivalent of b.h.p.}}{\text{heat content of fuel supplied}}$$

$$= \frac{\text{b.h.p.} \times 42\cdot416}{\text{lb/min of fuel} \times \text{calorific value}}$$

The units commonly used are:

In mechanical units —
1 hp = 33,000 ft lb/min = 1·0139 hp (metric)      1 hp (metric) = 4500 kgfm/min
    =    550 ft lb/sec = 76·044 kgfm/sec                        = 75 kgfm/sec

In electrical units —
1 hp = 0·7456 kW                                                        = 0·7355 kW.
    =    745·6 W                                                        = 735·5 W
    = 42·416 Btu/min = 23·57 Chu/min                          = 23·246 Chu/min
    = 0·707 Btu/sec    = 0·393 Chu/sec                          = 0·3875 Chu/sec

Whereas gas turbines derive their power from the inertia of the mass of gases passing through them and impinging on the turbine blades, the power output of positive displacement engines, including rotary piston engines, relies upon gas pressure. It stands to reason, therefore, that certain fundamental relationships, as established for reciprocating piston engines, may also apply to rotary piston designs provided the mechanism of these engines facilitates volume variations as required for the preferred thermodynamic cycle. One point which has been proved is that carrying the whole mass of the mixture round a more or less oval path does not impose any limitations on the actual combustion process, or indeed on engine speed. This finding had, to some extent, already been confirmed in early research work by Sir Harry Ricardo, but photographic and other proof has since been accumulated by those participating in NSU/Wankel developments. Moreover, the mere mechanical configuration of the rotary piston engine could not be suspected to have more than marginal effects. Indeed, it ought to be noted that only one breakaway torque occurs in a rotary engine, whereas something akin to this has to be overcome at the end of every stroke in reciprocating piston engines, the condition becoming progressively worse as cylinder wear takes place because piston rings tend to wear circular grooves near to top and bottom dead centre and must in effect be wrenched out before the piston can continue to move.

Another fundamental relationship, (see Fig. 10.1) namely that between thermal efficiency and compression ratio, also applies to RC engines. Efficiency rises as the compression ratio increases, the gain being more appreciable at the lower ratios up to about 10 to 1 when the somewhat empirical curve begins to flatten out. The highest practical compression ratio depends upon the octane rating of the fuel and the temperature at which self-ignition could occur. The NSU/Wankel RC engine would seem to offer an advantage here as the absence of the exhaust valves avoids the hot spot, which is most difficult to control, from within the combustion chamber. Furthermore, the absence of valves prevents any possible and calamitous contact between valves and piston crown should engine speed get out of hand.

Assuming that conventional engineering materials are to be used, as for instance various grades of cast iron, aluminium alloys and steel, it is imperative to take into account the effects of differential thermal expansion. On the assumption that a cast iron rotor of 2·5 in axial length is required to operate in an aluminium housing at a running clearance of 0·002–0·003 in, the actual clearance at the operating wall temperature of 360°F (182·22°C) shows an increase of ·0072–·0082 in. If the length of the sealing path amounts to 15 in the resulting leakage area is 0·108 to 0·123 $in^2$ or the equivalent of a square hole measuring 0·3286 in × 0·3286 in to 0·357 in × 0·357 in

The art of modern production design and engineering is to ensure that every component is made within the widest limits without sacrificing either quality or functional requirements of the mechanism for which it is destined. The closer the limit the higher the production cost and the greater the number of components which have to be scrapped. Moreover, it is hardly sensible to insist on tolerances of ±0·0005 in if the respective dimension alters 0·01 in under operating conditions.

The NSU/Wankel rotary piston engine is an assembly of a central housing and two end covers, the concentricity of the bore and the eccentric shaft will also fluctuate within certain cumulative limits. Taking into account the unavoidable clearance between the shaft and its bearings it may easily be necessary to accommodate additional fluctuation of the actual clearances between the rotor and the bore. It is, therefore, the purpose of a sealing system to prevent any leakage paths despite differential thermal expansion, shaft deflections and manufacturing tolerances and limits. Caution, however, seems prudent in these days when the use of unorthodox engineering materials, such as certain types of ceramics, is accelerating. Should it be possible to produce rotors and housings from material which, in engineering terms, expands only a negligible amount over the requisite temperature range, it may become necessary to re-examine the position to see whether a sealing system is still imperative.

So far it has been found that the attainment of a reasonable compression ratio and the accommodation of a sensible sealing arrangement are essential features of rotary piston engines. In addition it was indicated that certain parts of rotary piston engines may be made from some non-metallic materials, ceramics for example, which may obviate or reduce the need for the incorporation of special sealing devices and thereby reduce the friction losses of the engine.

Although the maximum speeds of reciprocating piston engines are rising, and more and more power is being coaxed from them, it is evident that these results are achieved through enormous and costly research efforts. Despite the rising engine costs thereby incurred, the inherent limitations due to the reciprocating masses of the valve actuating mechanism, as well as of the piston/connecting rod assemblies, have merely been stretched in proportion to the reduction of the reciprocating masses or the higher stress levels permitted by the use of superior materials. For example, M. R. McKellar of General Motor Corporation's Pontiac Motor Division wrote in his S.A.E. paper No. 660126 of January 1966 'A comparison of the 1966 overhead cam system with the 1965 push rod operated valve mechanism reveals significant advantages for the 1966 overhead cam design. Number and weight of moving parts required to actuate the valves has been reduced. Actual total weight of parts driven by the camshaft has been reduced by 45%, while the

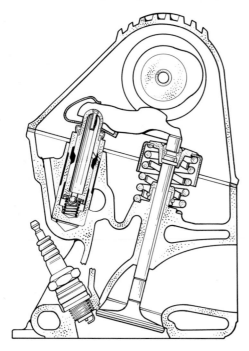

*Fig. 2.2. Overhead camshaft and valve mechanism of 1966 Pontiac Tempest six cylinder engine. The camshaft is driven by a neoprene timing belt containing continuously wound glass fibre cords, which are arranged to run on the theoretical pitch diameter of the sprockets and are intended to take the driving tension*

effective inertia at the valve was reduced by 27% (See Fig. 2.2.). These points are emphasised by the following data pertaining to the two engines in question:

**Table 2.1**

| Engine | Year | Compression Ratio | Displacement $(in^3)$ | b.h.p.—rev/min (hp) | Torque—rev/min (lb ft) |
|--------|------|-------------------|----------------------|---------------------|------------------------|
| Standard | 1965 | 8.6 to 1 | 215 | 140—4200 | |
| | 1966 | 9.0 to 1 | 230 | 165—4700 | 216—2600 |
| 4 Barrel Carb. | 1966 | 10.5 to 1 | 230 | 207—5200 | 228—3800 |

It may be concluded from Felix Wankel's book 'Rotary Piston Machines' (Iliffe Books Ltd., London), that rotary piston engines should not be subjected to limitations which may be imposed by reciprocating masses or by masses having variable angular velocity.

Further analysis of central axis SROM designs (Table 9, line IX, columns 17–20 in the above book, commonly referred to as 'cat and mouse engines'), see also Fig. 2.3 and Fig. 2.4, show the Kauertz and Maier engines for which different mechanisms were evolved to give the respective rotary pistons variable angular velocity, which is in fact superimposed on the general rotary motion. Ingenious though these mechanisms may be, it is evident

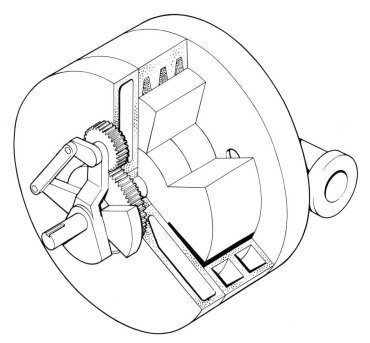

Fig. 2.3. The Kauertz 'Cat and Mouse' type engine. Variations of the volumes between the rotors is effected by the planetary gearing and the crank and connecting link arrangement

that their variable angular velocities and consequential inertia forces make extraordinary demands on their gears, cranks, connecting rods or slides. Therefore they impose the same if not more stringent limitations than those due to the valve gear of reciprocating piston engines. For this reason it is preferable if the variable volume chambers, as required for the respectively chosen thermodynamic cycle, are formed without recourse to such complex mechanisms. Avoidance of inertia forces due to non-uniform rotary motion also avoids stress and durability limitations. Indeed, the Renault-American Motors, the Japanese Isuzu and the NSU/Wankel configurations prove that the absence of components moving at non-uniform angular velocities is a practicable and indeed desirable feature. The higher speed and performance potential of rotary piston engines can only be achieved if all rotating components have uniform velocity.

It is no secret that induction and exhaust systems determine engine performance characteristics. Though rather complex, and sometimes contradictory, these influences must be taken into account, but their interplay is seldom fully appreciated, nor are they easy to explain. Engine power output depends upon a continuous supply of suitably

atomised and vaporised fuel suspended in an appropriate amount of air. The correct
mixture composition, as required for complete combustion, cannot be supplied and is not
required under all operating conditions. It is the function of the carburettor and the
throttle to measure out and atomise the fuel, besides admitting the requisite amount of

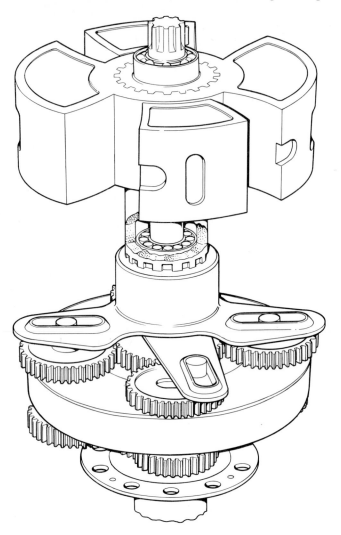

*Fig. 2.4. The Maier engine. The rather substantial rotors are moved at
variable angular velocity by the somewhat complex planetary gearing
and the crank-slider arrangement to form the variable volume chambers
of the engine.*

air. The addition of heat to facilitate vaporisation and thereby promote satisfactory
ignition and combustion may be the function of the induction system, the combustion
chamber or both. In practice this division of labour is simple and automatic, except that
if an automotive installation is under consideration the throttle remains under the driver's

control. Whenever the accelerator pedal is released, the throttle closes, with the result that suction pressure between the throttle and the valve will be lower than that between the throttle and the choke or Venturi. In terms of ambient conditions, less mixture will get into the engine under these circumstances, and proportionately less than maximum power will be developed.

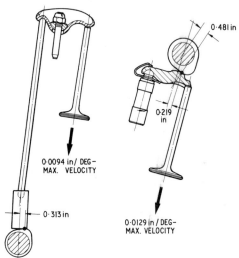

Fig. 2.5. *It is obvious that the overhead camshaft design consists of fewer parts and, in addition, the reciprocating masses are considerably reduced*

When the throttle is wide open the critical restriction occurs at the inlet valves, and the engine is, in this respect, set for the development of its maximum power.

No indication has been given in the preceding paragraphs to permit the conclusion that different considerations apply to reciprocating and rotary piston engines. Figs. 2.5 and 2.6 suggest that considerable attention is devoted to the valve actuating and induction system designs, which control the quantity and quality of the combustion mixture. In this connection it is particularly instructive to examine the data contained in the

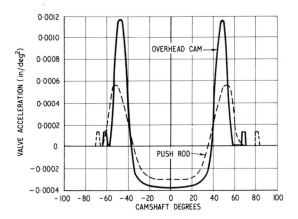

Fig. 2.6. *Comparison of valve acceleration of overhead cam versus push rod valve actuation*

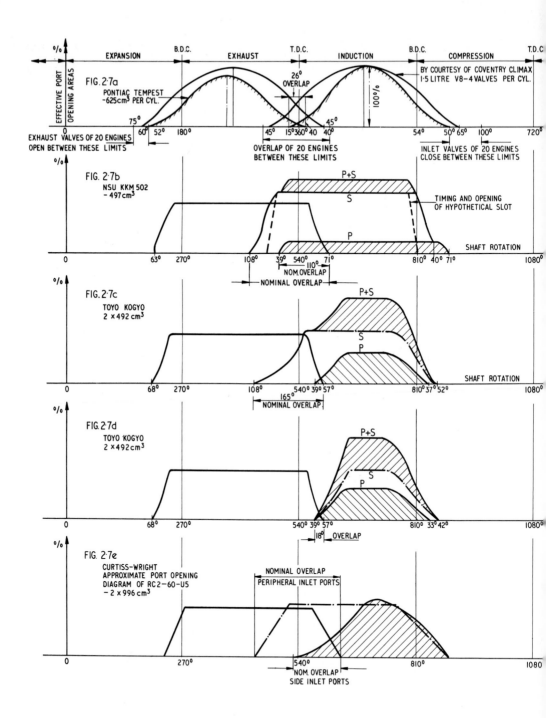

FIG. 2·7a
PONTIAC TEMPEST
-625cm³ PER CYL.

BY COURTESY OF COVENTRY CLIMAX
1·5 LITRE V8-4 VALVES PER CYL.

EXHAUST VALVES OF 20 ENGINES OPEN BETWEEN THESE LIMITS
OVERLAP OF 20 ENGINES BETWEEN THESE LIMITS
INLET VALVES OF 20 ENGINES CLOSE BETWEEN THESE LIMITS

FIG. 2·7b
NSU KKM 502
- 497cm³

TIMING AND OPENING OF HYPOTHETICAL SLOT

SHAFT ROTATION

NOM. OVERLAP
NOMINAL OVERLAP

FIG. 2·7c
TOYO KOGYO
2 × 492 cm³

SHAFT ROTATION

NOMINAL OVERLAP

FIG. 2·7d
TOYO KOGYO
2 × 492 cm³

OVERLAP

FIG. 2·7e
CURTISS-WRIGHT
APPROXIMATE PORT OPENING
DIAGRAM OF RC2-60-U5
- 2 × 996 cm³

NOMINAL OVERLAP
PERIPHERAL INLET PORTS

NOM. OVERLAP
SIDE INLET PORTS

20014345

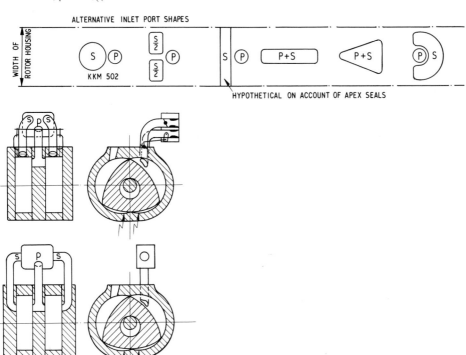

ALTERNATIVE INLET PORT SHAPES

WIDTH OF ROTOR HOUSING

KKM 502

HYPOTHETICAL ON ACCOUNT OF APEX SEALS

*Fig. 2.7a. Comparison of valve opening and timing of Pontiac Tempest o.h.c. engine (626 cm³ per cylinder) with four valve o.h.c. Coventry Climax V8 racing engine (187 cm³ per cylinder) — by courtesy of Coventry Climax and Pontiac Motor Division — illustrating how attempts are made to improve gas flow to and from the cylinders in pursuit of higher performance*

*Fig. 2.7b. The two stage induction system of the NSU KKM 502 RC engine is clearly seen. The primary port is in use at idling speed, and at low loads, from which point onward the much larger secondary port becomes operative by opening of the throttle valve. The diagram illustrates essentially port openings and overlap of a high performance engine*

*Fig. 2.7c. Toyo Kogyo introduced an interesting variant by combining side primary with peripheral secondary inlet ports to obtain the best of two worlds, namely improved performance at both extremes of the load and speed ranges*

*Fig. 2.7d. The same aims were satisfied as with the configuration shown in 2.7c, except that both primary and secondary inlet ports are side ports. It may be concluded that this engine is potentially more suitable for saloon cars rather than high performance sports cars*

*Fig. 2.7e. Curtiss-Wright have also investigated peripheral and side inlet ports. It appears that at the moment side inlet ports are favoured for engines required to operate over a wide load and speed range, as for instance car engines, whereas peripheral ports are considered for aircraft and other applications. Development of direct fuel injection systems and techniques may alter the situation in favour of peripheral inlet ports*

'Valve Train Design Specification' of the new Pontiac overhead-camshaft six cylinder engine, and especially the comparison between the standard single barrel carburettor engine and the high compression four barrel carburettor overhead cam engine version.

Table 2.2. VALVE TRAIN DESIGN SPECIFICATIONS

|  | One Barrel Carburettor | | Four Barrel Carburettor |
| --- | --- | --- | --- |
|  | OHV 1965 | OHC 1966 | OHC 1966 |
| Total Valve Event (Crankshaft Degrees) | 252° | 228° | 244° |
| Maximum Valve Lift (Intake and Exhaust) | 0·333 in | 0·400 in | 0·438 in |
| Height of Opening Ramp at Valve | 0·00439 in | 0·00283 in | 0·00283 in |
| Height of Closing Ramp at Valve | 0·00723 in | 0·00633 in | 0·00633 in |
| Peak Velocity | 0·0094 in/deg | 0·0129 in/deg | 0·01248 in/deg |
| Peak Valve Acceleration | 0·000568 in/deg$^2$ | 0·00117 in/deg$^2$ | 0·000841 in/deg$^2$ |
| Maximum Rate of Acceleration | 0·0000638 in/deg$^3$ | 0·0002 in/deg$^3$ | 0·0001166 in/deg$^3$ |
| Nominal Total Valve Overlap (Crankshaft Degrees) | 38° | 14° | 26° |
| Intake Valve Opening (Before Top Centre) | 18° | 7° | 15° |
| Intake Valve Closing (After Bottom Centre) | 54° | 41° | 50° |
| Exhaust Valve Opening (Before Bottom Centre) | 52° | 41° | 52° |
| Exhaust Valve Closing (After Top Centre) | 20° | 7° | 11° |

As the performance of rotary piston engines also depends upon the admission of a satisfactory amount and quality of mixture, it is obvious that equally meticulous attention is required for the preparation and admission of such mixtures. However, there is reason to believe that the fundamental differences between the reciprocating and rotary piston engines must be taken into account. For instance, in the case of peripheral inlet and exhaust ports, the port opening diagrams are different from valve opening diagrams, see Figs. 2.7a–e. Moreover, far more rapid opening and closing periods can be provided by suitable shaping of the ports, see Fig. 2.7b. In the absence of valves and their actuating gear, no consideration need be given to their overriding limiting effects. Care is necessary to ensure adequate mixture turbulence, which is so conveniently promoted by the valves in four-stroke reciprocating piston engines. Fig. 2.7b shows the actual port opening and closing diagram of the KKM 502 engine as fitted to the NSU/Spider car; also shown are the steepest port opening and closing curves, theoretically attainable when the port is reduced to a rectangular slot right across the centre housing. This comparison is based upon the assumption that gas velocity and engine speed demand the same cross-sectional area as provided for the KKM 502 engine. By implication the most gradual port opening and closing curves are obtainable if the port opening is a long narrow rectangle whose beginning and end is determined by timing consideration. Any amount of variation between the two extremes are possible, as for instance sudden opening and gradual closing as engine performance characteristics may demand. So far it has been found that adequate performance is obtainable with round and slightly oval port shapes.

These maximum slope opening and closing curves are only of academic significance as long as apex seals are indispensible. Moreover the shape and slope of these curves may be altered by shaping the ports at the merging point with the epitrochoidal bore to suit the specific engine application and performance characteristics. It will be necessary to elaborate on this point in the appropriate chapter of this book.

With regard to port timing of Wankel RC engines, it is obvious that port shapes and their relative positions can affect the entire performance characteristics of an RC engine. This means that the design is more flexible than is possible with a poppet valve four-stroke engine. This flexibility may be desirable but it adds to the task confronting the designer.

Valve timing of conventional engines is given relative to crankshaft position, that is relative to t.d.c. or b.d.c., which represents, in fact, piston displacement or displacement volume. Direct comparison of the reciprocating piston valve timing with the port timing of the Wankel RC engine is made more complicated because every phase extends over 270° shaft rotation, whereas every stroke of the reciprocating piston engine extends over 180° crankshaft movement if overlap is ignored. Hence 30° of port overlap in the Wankel RC engine is the equivalent of 20° valve opening overlap in a four stroke poppet valve engine. Further consideration would lead, of course, to the study of port opening relative to volumetric displacement and comparison of this with valve opening relative to piston displacement, it being obvious that the pattern of exhaust gas and mixture velocity in these two types of engines will differ on account of the differences in effective inlet and exhaust port and valve openings.

Figs. 2.7c and d show the approximate port timing of the Toyo Kogyo twin rotor engine whose single chamber displacement (492 cm$^3$) is virtually the same as that of the KKM 502 engine. This engine was conceived in several versions

1. With a three barrel carburettor and combination side and peripheral inlet ports, defined as primary and secondary ports which are opened and closed relative to each other with customary throttle type valves.
2. With a three barrel carburettor with primary and secondary inlet ports, all side ports and in continuous use.
3. The same as (2) but with a two barrel carburettor.
4. The latest production version of this engine is equipped with a specially developed four barrel type carburettor.

For differentiation between nominal and actual or effective port opening overlap periods see Chapter 8.

From a practical point of view it is obvious that rotary piston engines should not be more complicated or costly to produce than equivalent reciprocating piston engines used for identical purposes. The only seemingly justifiable deviation from this maxim would be phenomenally superior engine efficiency, performance and durability so as to minimise the effects of complexity and higher costs. (see Plate 2.1)

In summing up it may be reiterated that the essential features of any successful rotary piston engine are:

1. *A sensible thermodynamic cycle which facilitates the highest feasible thermal efficiency.*
2. *The design must be capable of accommodating an efficient sealing grid which can block*

*any possible leakage path between the respective working chambers, and between these chambers and the environmental atmosphere.*

3. *All rotating parts ought to move at a uniform angular velocity and all reciprocating masses should be avoided.*

4. *Port cross-sectional areas and timing must be commensurate with the expected performance range of the engine — a surprisingly large number of rotary piston engine designs appear to be incapable of providing this indispensable feature.*

5. *Simplicity and manufacturing costs of rotary piston engines must compare favourably with those of equal power conventional engines designed for the same applications and produced in equal numbers. The implication is that engine bulk and weight of materials used must not be of such an order, especially for car engines, that their cost together with indispensable production facilities makes the rotary piston engine much more expensive to produce.*

6. *For a given size and weight of engine the power output should be at least the same as for reciprocating piston engines.*

It is, of course, possible to elaborate on every one of these fundamental requirements and add, for instance, that the potential of the rotary piston engine for further development must show promise of exceeding the capabilities of the conventional reciprocating piston engine. Greater emphasis may be preferred on essential auxiliaries such as the ignition system. Alternatively it may be considered that the service-free life of these engines should be stressed, but the purpose of this chapter is to draw attention to some fundamental features expected of rotary piston engines rather than attempt the impossible and write a specification for ideal or perfect rotary engines. Besides, engines are usually designed with specific applications in mind, which make their own peculiar demands.

Whichever way one looks at it, there is no doubt that a profusion of considerations must be taken into account during the design stage of a rotary piston engine. Some of these points are the same as must be considered for reciprocating piston engines, others are peculiar to one type of engine or the other. The NSU/Wankel concept has the distinction of being the first rotary piston configuration capable of satisfying all these stipulations, besides holding out a promise of substantially exceeding the performance and durability levels of the conventional reciprocating piston engine.

# 3

# The Epitrochoidal Configuration

Felix Wankel had long recognised the indispensable features of rotary piston internal combustion engines when, in 1954, he found that by rotating an equilateral triangle in a certain manner relative to a containing member, three variable volume chambers could be formed between them. The pattern of volume variations seemed to satisfy the requirements of the four-stroke or Otto-cycle, whilst adequate sealing appeared possible by incorporating the now familiar Wankel sealing grid. The locus of every apex of this equilateral triangle was oval with a slight necking in on the minor axis and was subsequently identified as an epitrochoid. Of course, it is possible to construct or generate epitrochoids or hypotrochoids with any number of lobes, requiring their own peculiarly shaped rotors, as indicated in Fig. 3.1, and more are shown in 'Rotary Piston Machines'*. The designation of the NSU/Wankel engine according to this classification is PLM 2:3 Sli, which stands for 'Planetary rotation engine with a lobe/flank ratio of 2:3, slip engagement and the sealing elements or epitrochoidal generating points are accommodated in the inner member (equilateral rotor)'. With reference to Fig. 2.7, it is evident that adequate port sizes and opening periods can be accommodated, thus the prerequisites of a workable rotary piston engine were given by this particular configuration.

## 3.1. Derivation of Epitrochoids from First Principles

By definition an epitrochoid or prolate cycloid is the locus of a point on the radius of a circle which is rolling, without slip, round the outside of a base circle. To obtain the familiar two lobe epitrochoidal bore of the Wankel RC engine the base circle radius must be twice the rolling circle radius so that the rolling circle makes exactly two revolutions during every complete orbit round the base circle, as in Fig. 3.2.

*Felix Wankel's Classification of purely rotary pumps, compressors and engines etc (see Reference 2, Chapter 1).

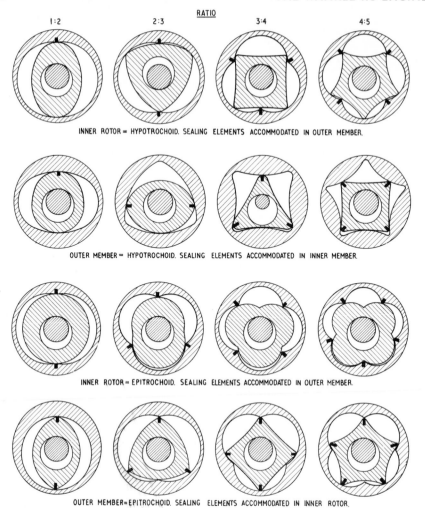

RATIO

Fig. 3.1. The multiplicity of possible configurations is by no means exhausted by the sixteen hypotrochoidal and epitrochoidal designs shown. The ratios given at the top indicate the relative speeds of the outer or inner rotor — even if one member is stationary and its rotational speed has been transferred to the crankshaft

The fundamental proportions of an epitrochoid are base circle radius $= r_0 = 2r$, rolling circle radius $= r$ and the distance $e$ of the generating point from the rolling circle centre.

Furthermore, it is convenient to note that $r_0 + r = 3r = R$. Hence the major diameter of the epitrochoid becomes $2(R+e)$                                                                   (3.1)

and the minor diameter of the epitrochoid becomes $2(R-e)$                                            (3.2).

Before proceeding further it should be pointed out that there has been mention else-where of a so-called $K$ factor, $K = R/e$. This is deprecated, as the ratio of $R/e$ is clearly understood even by those unfamiliar with rotary engine manufacture, whilst there are already a profusion of $K$ factors in science and engineering.

Plotting an epitrochoid as shown in Fig. 3.2 is not easy. In fact mechanical aids would seem desirable. In addition, the relationship between this configuration and the Wankel RC engine is not immediately recognised by the uninitiated, a shortcoming which is easily corrected by the following method of construction (see Fig. 3.3):

I. Draw a circle radius $e$.

II. Divide this circle into equal parts (say 24, as shown, making adjacent radii 15° apart). Number the points where the radii intersect the circle (in this example 1–12 on either side of $Oy$).

III. Draw from each numbered point a fairly long line progressively inclined at an angle of 5° from the last, commencing with the lines from the first points each side of $Oy$ at 5° to $Oy$, as shown.

IV. Construct an equilateral triangle on a piece of tracing paper, making each side $2R \sin 60 (= 1·7321R)$. The lines from the apexes ($A$, $B$, $C$) of the triangle bisecting their respective opposite sides will intersect at the centre of gravity ($O'$) of the triangle, and the distances $O'A$, $O'B$ and $O'C$ will be $R$.

V. Place this tracing on the figure drawn according to I–III above in the manner shown in Fig. 3.3 (i.e. with $O'C$ lying along the line drawn from point 1 as described in III above). As the triangle is moved round all the numbered points and $O'C$ aligned with the lines drawn from them the locus of the apexes $A$, $B$ and $C$ will produce the same epitrochoidal bore as that obtained by the first method.

It is interesting to note that although the relative position of $e$ and $R$ are reversed, the generated curve is an epitrochoid. In this instance $e$ denotes visibly the eccentricity of the

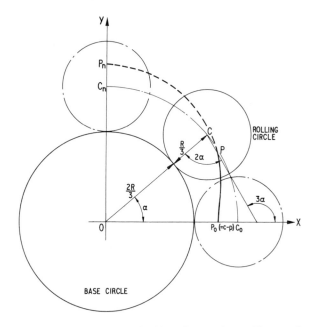

Fig. 3.2.   Generating epitrochoid by rolling circle round base circle.
Epitrochoid is the locus of point P on the radius of the rolling circle

Library
Sampson Technical Institute

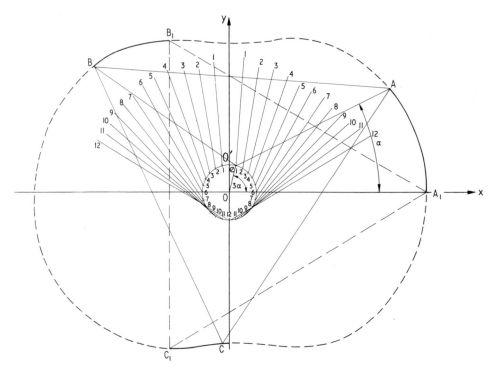

Fig. 3.3. Alternatively an epitrochoid may be described as the locus of the apexes of an equilateral triangle which — for the Wankel RC configuration — rotates at one-third shaft speed, i.e. for every 15° shaft displacement the rotor moves through 5°

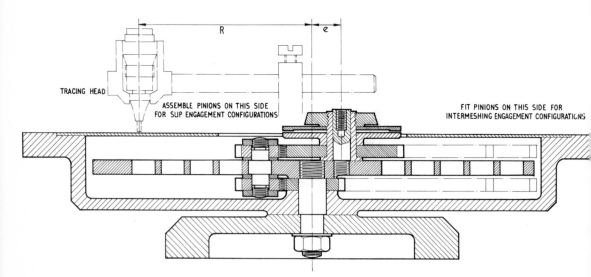

Fig. 3.4. This relatively simple mechanism, devised at TES, may be used to draw different trochoidal configurations and permits the study of port timing

output shaft of the NSU/Wankel engine, which rotates at three times the speed of the rotor, and the rotor or its apex seals are necessarily in continuous contact with the epitrochoidal bore. The vertical and horizontal ordinates for every point on the epitrochoidal curve are, from Fig. 3.2

$$\left.\begin{array}{l} Y_A = R \sin \alpha \\ Y_e = R \sin \alpha - e \sin 3\alpha \end{array}\right\} \qquad (3.3)$$

where $\alpha$ = angular displacement of $R$ from horizontal axis;
Similarly

$$\left.\begin{array}{l} X_A = R \cos \alpha \\ X_e = R \cos \alpha - e \cos 3\alpha \end{array}\right\} \qquad (3.4)$$

where $X$ is the horizontal ordinate and suffixes $A$ and $e$ denote the respective ordinate of point $A$ and $e$, $e$ being on the epitrochoid.

It should also be noted that $\alpha = \omega_1 \cdot t$ $\qquad (3.5)$

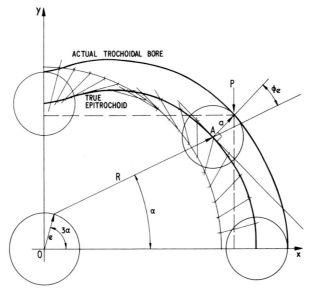

Fig. 3.5. The rectangular co-ordinates of any point P on the actual trochoidal bore, which is parallel to the true epitrochoid and distance a outside it, are:

$$x = e \cos Z\alpha + R \cos \alpha + a \cos (\alpha + \phi_e)$$
$$y = e \sin Z\alpha + R \sin \alpha + a \sin (\alpha + \phi_e)$$

$$\cos \phi_e = \frac{R + Ze \cos (Z-1)\alpha}{[(Ze)^2 + R^2 + 2ZeR \cos (Z-1)\alpha]^{\frac{1}{2}}}$$

For the familiar Wankel RC engine configuration $Z = 3$ and $\phi_e$ is the effective angle of obliquity for any position P on the trochoidal curve

Hence
$$x = e \cos 3\alpha + R \cos \alpha + a \cos (\alpha + \phi_e) \qquad (3.3a)^*$$
$$y = e \sin 3\alpha + R \sin \alpha + a \sin (\alpha + \phi_e) \qquad (3.4a)$$

$$\cos \phi_e = \frac{R + 3e \cos 2\alpha}{[9e^2 + R^2 + 6eR \cos 2\alpha]^{\frac{1}{2}}}$$

$\phi_e$ is a maximum when it equals $\phi$, that is when $\cos 2\alpha = \dfrac{-3e}{R}$

$\phi_e$ is the effective angle of obliquity at any point P
*cf. Equations 3.3 and 3.4

There is no doubt at all that these laborious methods of generating an epitrochoid on the drawing board are far too time-consuming for a design office where serious work on the development of the Wankel configurations is contemplated. A generating mechanism as shown in Fig. 3.4 may prove invaluable not merely because it speeds the physical drawing process, but also because it facilitates investigations as to port opening and closing periods. It may prove particularly useful to construct a generating machine where either $e$ may be varied to suit or fixing $e = 10$ mm and altering $R$ to give the desired relationship for a particular design. In the latter case the generated figure will be to scale in the ratio of $(e/e_o)^2$ where $e$ is the actual $e$ required and $e_o = 10$ mm.

It is emphasised that making the bore of a Wankel RC engine a true epitrochoid would force the apex seals to move slightly in and out of their respective slots as the contact line between apex seals and bore moves round the noses of these apex seals. This additional movement, or more precisely the resulting cyclic inertia forces, may prove a contributory factor to the formation of chatter marks on the bore surface, which ultimately lead to lubrication and wear problems besides loss of power. Having generated a true epitrochoid it is fairly easy to obtain the equidistant curve by drawing numerous short arcs of radius $a$ and the tangent to all these arcs will be the equidistant curve or true bore of the proposed design. If little more than an accurate drawing is required, and a generating machine is used, the simpler solution is to increase the length of the generating radius by the distance $a$, that is $R_1 = R+a$, as in Fig. 3.5, which seems sufficiently accurate for various performance and other calculations. For manufacturing purposes or when it is necessary to produce the bore within strict limits, the ordinates must be accurately calculated rather than relying upon the simplified construction method.

## 3.2. The Rotor Contour—How it is obtained

According to the foregoing we can now draw and generate the epitrochoidal bore as required for the Wankel RC engine, but Fig. 3.6 suggests that flanks of the equilateral triangle or rotor ought to be convex shaped without actually touching the bore at any point in whatever position they may be. The desirability of this is based on two considerations of particular significance for compressors and internal combustion engines, namely:

1. The minimum volume trapped between a rotor flank and the bore should be as small as possible.
2. The minimum volume trapped between a rotor flank and the bore must facilitate the attainment of the desired (or the highest possible) compression ratio as this has determining effects on thermal efficiency. (Thermal efficiency $= 1-(1/\varepsilon)^{\gamma-1}$ where $\varepsilon$ is the compression ratio).

The highest theoretical compression ratio is obtained if the rotor flank contour is generated similar to the epitrochoid, except that instead of marking every apex in the consecutive positions it will be necessary to trace part of the true bore on either side of the minor axis. The common tangent to all these curves will be the rotor flank contour. Running clearances, thermal expansion and manufacturing tolerances necessitate that

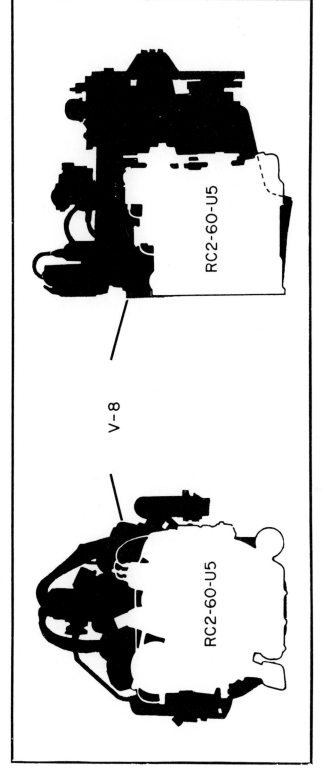

*Plate 2.1a. Comparison of RC2-60-U5 with current American V8 engine developing about the same b.h.p. (First published by Curtiss-Wright in SAE 650723)*

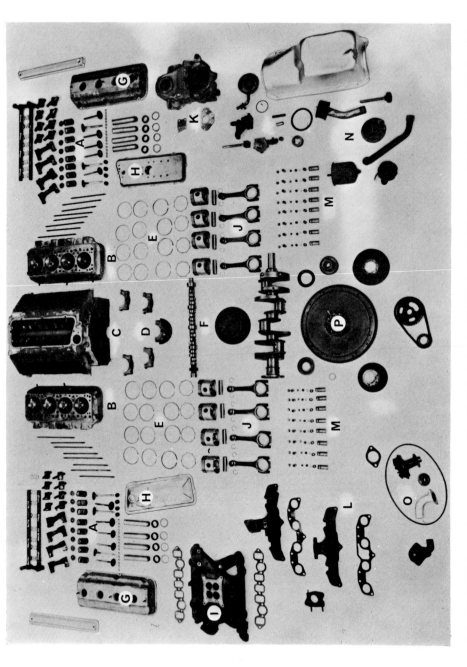

Plate 2.1b. (A) Valves and rocker arm assembly, (B) Cylinder block, (D) Bearings, (E) Piston Rings, (F) Camshaft, (G) Valve Covers, (H) Breather panels, (I) Intake system, (J) Piston and rod assemblies, (K) Accessory drive housing, (L) Exhaust system, (M) Hydraulic valve assemblies, (N) Oil system, (O) Cooling system, (P) Mainshaft balance assembly

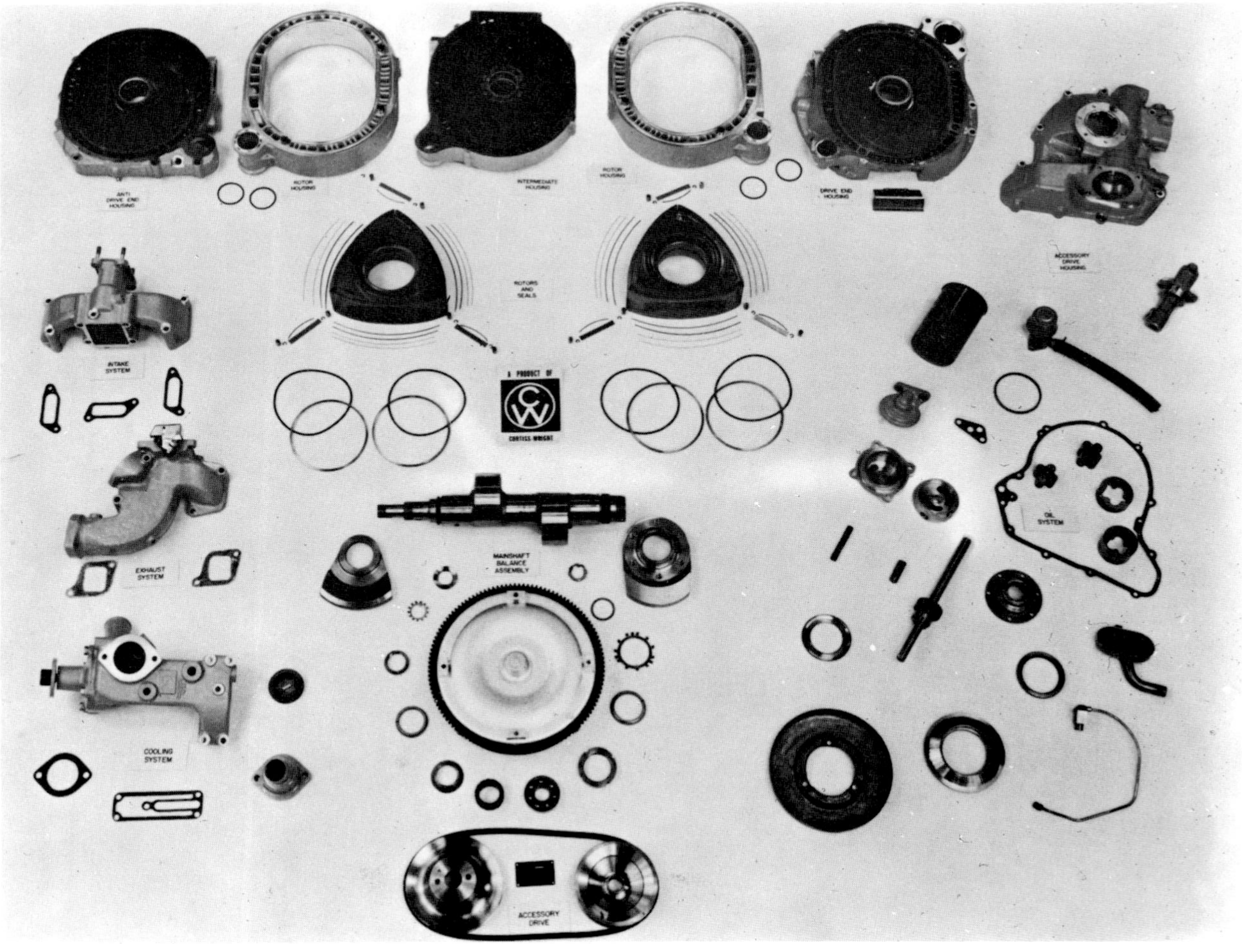
ANTI
DRIVE END
HOUSING
ROTOR
HOUSING
INTERMEDIATE
HOUSING
ROTOR
HOUSING
DRIVE END
HOUSING
ACCESSORY
DRIVE
HOUSING
ROTORS
AND
SEALS
INTAKE
SYSTEM
A PRODUCT OF
CW
CURTISS-WRIGHT
OIL
SYSTEM
EXHAUST
SYSTEM
MAINSHAFT
BALANCE
ASSEMBLY
COOLING
SYSTEM
ACCESSORY
DRIVE

Plate 2.1c.

Plate 4.1. Partly sectioned view of original single rotation (SIM) type engine in which the equilateral rotor and the member containing the epitrochoidal bore rotated about their own respective centres. This engine displaced 125 cm³ and developed 29·5 b.h.p.

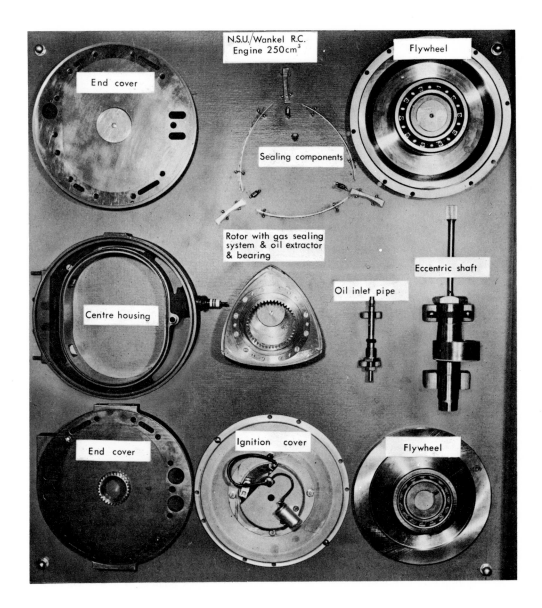

Plate 5.1. Components of early experimental single rotor PLM engine. This type of engine displaced 250 cm³ (15 in³) per shaft revolution, developed 36 b.h.p. at 6,000 rev/min, and weighed 66 lb. This was the first NSU/ Wankel RC type engine installed in a car

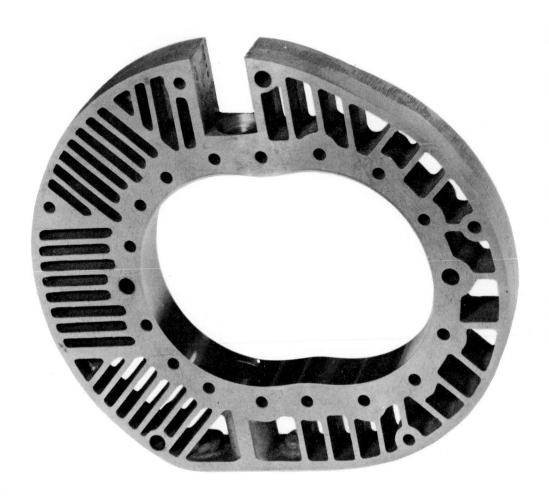

Plate 10.1. Centre Housing of Fichtel & Sachs air cooled industrial Wankel
RC engine. Note the crowding of the fins round the hot arch of the bore

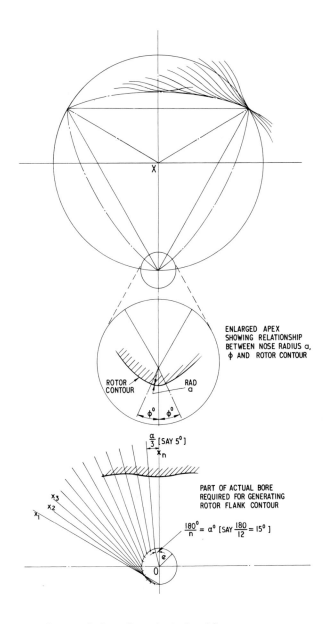

ENLARGED APEX
SHOWING RELATIONSHIP
BETWEEN NOSE RADIUS a,
φ AND ROTOR CONTOUR

ROTOR
CONTOUR

RAD
a

φ° φ°

$\frac{a}{3}$ [SAY 5°]

$x_n$

PART OF ACTUAL BORE
REQUIRED FOR GENERATING
ROTOR FLANK CONTOUR

$\frac{180°}{n} = a°$ [SAY $\frac{180}{12} = 15°$ ]

$x_3$
$x_2$
$x_1$

e

0

*Fig. 3.6. The rotor flank profile is obtained as follows:*
1. *Draw circle of radius e and divide half of it into n equal parts as shown*

2. *Radiating from each division o–n draw a line which makes an angle $\frac{\alpha}{3}$*

3. *Draw part of the actual epitrochoidal bore on either side of the minor axis as shown*
4. *Placing the drawing of the equilateral base triangle of the rotor on to the lines $x_1$ to $x_n$ so that the centre of the triangle is on the circle e, trace part of the actual bore*
   *The rotor contour (i.e. half flank contour) will be the common tangent to all the curves traced*
5. *For maximum compression ratio the flank contours match up to the nose radius (of apex seals) as shown in enlarged sketch of one apex*

the actual contour will be made somewhat smaller, depending on the material of the rotor and the housing.

If a rotor with contours generated as described rotates within its associated trochoidal bore, there would be virtually two separate variable volume chambers communicating with each other merely by way of the running clearance between the rotor flank and the bore within close proximity to the minor axis. Desirable though this may be on the side where the peripheral ports are situated, it would lead to completely unacceptable conditions on the combustion side. It was, therefore, found expedient to provide a fairly generous depression in every rotor flank, which results in a more compact and sensible combustion chamber shape, though it lowers the highest attainable compression ratio

$$\varepsilon = \frac{V_{max}}{V_{min}}$$

Under these circumstances it is doubtful whether the effort required to calculate the ordinates and the area between every side of the equilateral triangle and the actual profile is worthwhile, especially since it is perfectly satisfactory to rely upon the accuracy of a profile grinding machine for manufacturing purposes, whilst planimeter readings are adequate for calculating the volume.

If a scale drawing is available the planimeter readings will give the correct area directly, but if the standard 10 mm eccentricity of the generating mechanism is used, the planimeter readings must be multiplied by the factor $(e/e_o)^2$. To obtain the actual volume of this part of the rotor it is, of course, necessary to multiply this area by the rotor width, and the volume of the depression in the rotor flank must be subtracted from the value obtained. This point will be reconsidered in greater detail in Chapter 7 when elaborating on compression ratio and the relative volumetric displacement of the Wankel RC engine.

Strictly speaking, the rotor profile is a line parallel to and outside the true inner envelope of the trochoid, the distance between the two curves is, of course, distance $a$ minus the requisite running clearance. A theoretical approach to this complex issue is contained in the mathematical analysis at the end of this book, and further information is to be found in Prof. Othmar Baier's V.D.I. report No. 45, (1960).

## 3.3. Other configurations—Their advantages or limitations

Were it pertinent to point out the merits or disadvantages of the numerous possible RC engines, the opinion and conclusions expressed would be of rather hypothetical value as only comparatively modest research and development effort has so far been concentrated on designs other than the NSU/Wankel RC engine. It is significant that all those under development, however half-heartedly, rely upon the differential movement of rotor and housing to form the indispensable variable volume chambers. For instance, the original SIM type (single rotation) NSU/Wankel RC engine, the present PLM (planetary rotation) Wankel RC designs and the configuration under development at Renault in France, and at the American Motors Corporation in Detroit. In addition various design studies are in progress which aim at sorting out the manifold problems of

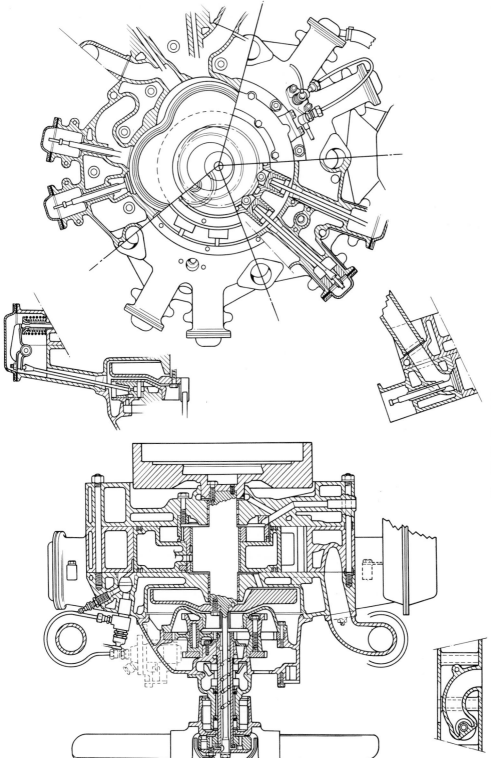

Fig. 3.7. The Renault/American Motors RC engine

multi-fuel and Diesel type RC engine design. Some of these configurations were, in fact, forecast at the time of the first authentic news releases about the NSU/Wankel venture and were as shown in Fig. 3.1.

The Renault/American Motors joint venture, Fig. 3.7, is based on the 1903 American Cooley steam engine, or possibly its RC engine derivative, the Umpleby design of 1909, which now reposes at the Museum in Keighley, Yorkshire.

In contrast with the Wankel concept of port timing being determined by rotor move-ment, the Renault/American Motors RC engine concept relies upon rotary disc or poppet valves for the admission of the combustible mixture and for the expulsion of the exhaust gases. Furthermore, the rotor does not push the gases round the bore; the thermodynamic phases, induction, compression, expansion and exhaust take place in five separate cham-bers with a receding bottom, the rotor. In this instance the sealing elements are accom-modated in the stationary housings and the rotor has a trochoidal shape. A complete sealing grid is required, i.e. sealing elements which block every possible leakage path, and are not easily incorporated — see Chapter 7. Even if an acceptable compromise solution to the vexed sealing problem is found, the introduction of the somewhat complex valve gear imposes its inherent limitations on this RC engine as it does on the conventional reciprocating piston engine.

Theoretically, the Renault RC engine concept would seem to be capable of achieving very high compression ratios. In practice the highest compression ratio which can be realised is determined by unavoidable port or valve opening periods. It seems, therefore, that piston-connecting rod assemblies have merely been replaced by a rotor and by an imperfect, more complex sealing system. No obvious features suggest that the potential of this type of RC engine could develop into a challenge to the reciprocating piston design. The poppet valve version may consist of marginally fewer components, but its proportions, which approach those of radial aircraft engines, may also pose an installation problem, at least for automobile applications. When full information on the performance of this type of engine is released revision of this opinion might be necessary.

Although no progress reports from Renault or the American Motors Corporation have been published, experiments carried out elsewhere suggest that this RC engine is as susceptible to chatter marks as the NSU/Wankel configuration used to be. Indeed Felix Wankel has made an elaborately instrumented test set-up, which incorporates a two lobe rotor as in the Cooley and Umpleby engines, for observation and close study of seal behaviour under actual operating conditions.

Some of the earliest news about the NSU/Wankel RC engine contained references to possible future interest in the 3:4 epitrochoidal configuration (Fig. 3.1) in which a four sided rotor moves in the manner of a planetary pinion in a three lobe epitrochoidal bore, the apex sealing elements being accommodated in the rotor. This arrangement provides an extra phase which could be utilised to obtain either an extended or even secondary expansion phase, or alternatively permit the attainment of much higher compression ratios. The pros and cons of these alternatives have their own respective protagonists. For example, the attainment of compression ratios to satisfy the Diesel cycle requirements without an additional supercharger seems attractive provided the expansion ratio, up to the instant of exhaust port opening, is long enough to permit efficient utilisation of the gas pressure and to prevent excessive noise and temperatures in the exhaust system. At the time of writing it appears that a more sensible all-round compromise can be obtained by incorporating a rotary type compressor — shaft driven — and allowing for an extended expansion period to reduce exhaust temperature and excessive noise. Clearly these issues are by no means fully resolved, particularly if it is borne in mind that a case could also be made out for a combination of RC engine with an exhaust turbo-supercharger or differential supercharging.

On this basis it may be emphasised that RC engines appear to be far more flexible and adaptable for the more sophisticated engine arrangements than the conventional reciprocating piston engine.

Regarding higher ratio configurations, that is a greater number of rotor flanks and bore lobes, it will be recognised that for a given individual chamber volume the overall size of the engine — pump, blower or compressor — increases as the number of these flanks and lobes increases. Similarly the shaft speeds must also be higher so that it is by no means a simple matter to decide on the relative merits of all the alternatives, assuming that all those considered are capable of providing adequate induction, compression, expansion and exhaust phases without sacrifice in other directions. For example, the epitrochoidal configurations in the third line of Fig. 3.1 may easily present sealing problems where the radial sealing elements change from contact with one rotor flank to contact with the succeeding flank.

For the time being at least it appears that on balance the Wankel RC design represents the most practical all-round technical and commercial compromise.

# 4

# The First Single Rotation (SIM) Type NSU/Wankel RC Engine

February 1st, 1957, was the memorable day on which the very first single rotation NSU/Wankel RC engine, Plate 4.1 and Fig. 4.1 began its faltering revolutions and soon developed measurable power, though only in short spurts. At the time it was difficult to decide whether this was an epoch-making event, but those present were decidedly relieved by their limited initial success. Since then it has become evident that RC type engines and, in particular, the kinematic inversion of the SIM configuration, namely planetary rotation engines, are capable of challenging the present monopoly of the reciprocating piston engine. Furthermore the potential for future development seems quite beyond reach of the reciprocating piston gasoline engine. Indeed, after modest attention to the cooling and sealing systems of the first prototype SIM engine, which had a maximum chamber volume of 125 cm$^3$, it developed 28·6 b.h.p. at 17,000 rev/min outer and 11,330 rev/min inner rotor speeds, whilst fuel consumption was 0·514 lb/b.h.p./hr and b.m.e.p. 120·9 lb/in$^2$.

Before elaborating on details of this design it may be opportune to define the 'Single Rotation Engine' (SIM). According to Felix Wankel's book, all the main components of an SIM machine rotate at uniform angular velocity about their own respective centres of gravity. Hence these machines may be completely and easily balanced and inertia or centrifugal forces do not add to the bearing loads caused by the gas forces. In addition the apex seals prescribe a true circular path, consequently no Coriolis forces tend to assist in promoting chatter phenomena. These cumulative characteristics make this type of engine eminently suitable for the highest rotational speeds.

The SIM type Wankel RC engine consists primarily of only two moving parts – inner and outer rotor – the main housing and suitable gearing which ensures correct relative rotation of the rotors. The distance between these two rotor centres, that is the axes of rotation, is *e*, whilst the bore of the outer rotor is of the now familiar epitrochoidal shape, and the contour of the inner rotor conforms with the so-called inner envelope of the epitrochoid. Three variable volume chambers are formed when these rotors move in the prescribed manner, and the pattern of volume variation satisfies the requirements of the Otto-cycle. For every two revolutions of the inner rotor, the outer and power transmitting component must make three revolutions and the correct relative movement is a

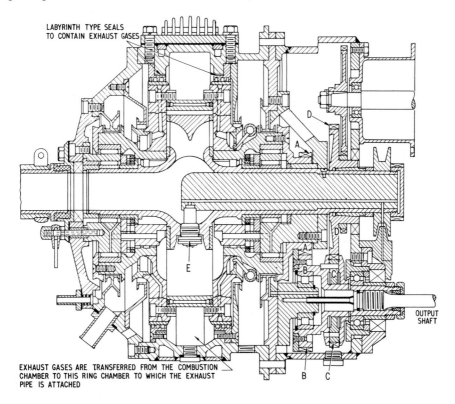

LABYRINTH TYPE SEALS
TO CONTAIN EXHAUST GASES

OUTPUT
SHAFT

EXHAUST GASES ARE TRANSFERRED FROM THE COMBUSTION
CHAMBER TO THIS RING CHAMBER TO WHICH THE EXHAUST
PIPE IS ATTACHED

*Fig. 4.1. Cross-sectional arrangement of original 125 cm³ SIM NSU/Wankel RC engine. Note gearing to ensure the correct relative rotation of the equilateral rotor and the rotating housing, which was the actual power transmitting part. Power is transmitted by gears A and B. Gears C and D are phasing gears controlling inner rotor movement. E = spark plug (one in each rotor flank)*

function of the gearing shown on the right hand side of Fig. 4.1. In fact, both rotors are geared to the output shaft but only the outer rotor is the power transmitting part since the resultant of the pressures on every inner rotor flank acts necessarily through the rotor centre, Fig. 4.2.

The carburettor is attached to a stationary, but co-axial, extension of the inner rotor shaft so that the mixture flows to the chambers by way of the hollow shaft, the rotor and suitably disposed transfer ports in the side members of the outer rotor. This ensures cooling of the inner rotor and of the spark plugs, which were fitted to every rotor flank, at small sacrifice of volumetric efficiency. Evidently it was no easy matter to clean the points or change a plug, though access may be gained by way of suitable apertures in the outer rotor and the main casing around it.

Ignition timing is by slip connections as shown on the right of Fig. 4.1.

Quite obviously this engine was made to prove the feasibility of Wankel's RC engine concept rather than for any specific application. For instance, both the main engine casing and the outer rotor are assemblies and exposed to variable temperatures and even pressures of the thermodynamic process, nevertheless they are expected to maintain adequate concentricity so that the outer rotor can run at high speed on two ordinary needle roller bearings at either extremity.

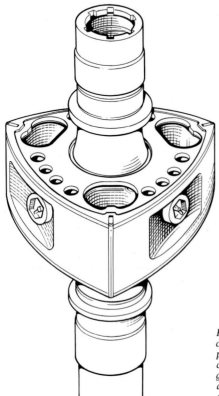

Fig. 4.2. Rotor of first SIM type NSU/Wankel RC engine. It could not transmit any forces as the resultant forces due to gas pressure on the flanks acted necessarily through the rotor centre which is also the geometric centre, i.e. the centre of gravity of the rotor. The sealing system incorporates apex seal and side sealing plates. Spark plugs are fitted in the depressions on every rotor flank

Although the principles of the sealing grid were incorporated, the sealing system as a whole was rather complex, see Fig. 4.3a and b. The essential features and operating conditions of a successful sealing grid will be considered in Chapter 7.

The single rotation engine is at present primarily of historical or hypothetical interest, but necessarily attention must be drawn to its mode of operation, or at least to certain features of it. Two methods of plotting epitrochoidal bores and rotor flank contours were considered in Chapter 3, it is therefore superfluous to reiterate how three variable volume chambers are formed and contained by the bore and the flanks of the equilateral rotor. Furthermore, it will be appreciated that the same three variable volume chambers can be formed if the equilateral rotor as well as the member containing the epitrochoidal bore move in a certain prescribed manner. As the inlet and outlet ports are fixed in the outer

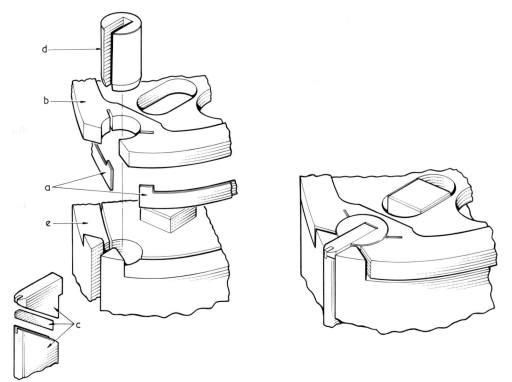

*Fig. 4.3a. The sealing arrangement of one of the first PLM type RC engines, which was complex and, therefore, costly*

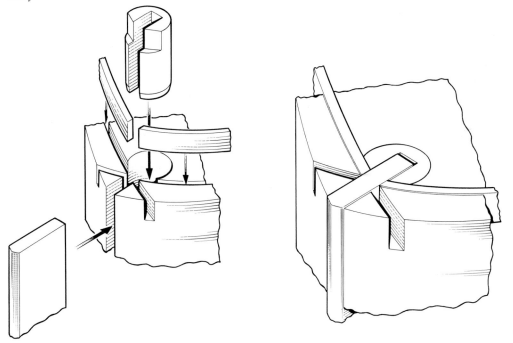

*Fig. 4.3b. A later and simpler sealing grid, which worked satisfactorily but presented interchangeability problems — see Fig. 7.5a and b for currently preferred sealing systems*

Library
Sampson Technical Institute

rotor there will be an induction period, a compression period, an expansion period and and exhaust period in every chamber, whilst the inner equilateral rotor describes a turn of 360° relative to the outer rotor or vice versa. This implies that every chamber volume varies twice from a minimum to a maximum per outer rotor revolution as required for the Otto-cycle.

The distance between the two axes of rotation is $e$. Considering the three inner rotor flanks it is clear that the resultant force due to pressure on every individual flank passes through the rotor centre, that is the axis about which the rotor revolves. Consequently no turning moment is obtained. On the other hand, action and reaction being equal and opposite, the same resultant forces do not, with the exception of one position, pass through the centre or axis of rotation of the outer rotor. A continuous turning moment is thereby produced which is related to the gas pressure acting within, and the device will develop power as is expected of any engine. It is possible that under certain circumstances and in a certain position, the turning moments due to the pressure on all three rotor flanks cancel each other out, but this is a momentary condition comparable with a single cylinder piston at top dead centre, the inertia of the rotating masses helping the machine over this point.

In explaining the mode of operation it is also clear that the primary purpose of gears C and D of Fig. 4.1 is to ensure the correct relative rotation of the inner rotor and over-come frictional forces, whereas A and B have to deal with engine torque and power output.

Despite the above-mentioned complexities of the actual design it must be admitted that there is a fascinating, if not compelling, simplicity in the whole conception of Felix Wankel's first successful RC engine.

# 5

# The Planetary Rotation Engine

Wankel and Hoeppner, his chief designer, had to choose between the SIM or PLM configurations once the feasibility of their basic concept was proved and a prototype design was required.

To Wankel the SIM configuration seemed akin to o.h.v. four-stroke engines, whereas the PLM design presented more formidable sealing problems because of the yet unproved linear sealing of the apex seals, and also because they follow epitrochoidal rather than circular paths. Moreover, exhaust and induction characteristics as well as speed limitations seemed to approach those of two-stroke engines. Cognisant of these problems, Dr. Ing. Walter Froede preferred the simpler PLM configuration for NSU.

The obvious difference between the SIM and Dr. Froede's PLM design (see Fig. 2.1 and Plate 5.1) is the stationary housing containing the epitrochoidal bore, which together with the rotor are identical in shape and proportions to those of the SIM engine. To achieve a design with a stationary housing and without an enveloping casing it became necessary to introduce a shaft with an eccentric portion to allow the rotor to move in the manner of a planetary pinion by rotating about its own centre of gravity, and simultaneously describe a perfect circle round the output shaft centre. The correct relative motion of the rotor and the eccentric shaft (1 to 3) is assured by an internal/external gear arrangement.

Concentrating the whole mass of the rotor on the eccentric portion of the output shaft necessitates provision for suitable balance weights outside the bearings, consequently the shaft must deal with a combination of bending and torsional loads, which may become critical in the higher performance and speed ranges. Though this shaft is probably stiffer than the crankshaft of an equivalent reciprocating piston engine, the resulting maximum stresses are high. Perhaps the most serious problems arising out of the PLM design were, until about 1964, associated with apex seal behaviour. As will be explained in greater detail in Chapter 7, the apex seals are guided by the rotor round the epitrochoidal bore, and are therefore subjected to varying centrifugal and Coriolis forces which, in combination with other phenomena, can promote the formation of chatter marks in certain parts of the bore. Despite this the kinematic inversion, which has since been justified, offered a worthwhile general simplification. In comparison with the original SIM design it offered fewer parts, greater flexibility in the choice of port size and timing, a wider choice of effective compression ratios, easy access to the ignition plug, improved cooling, easing of the lubrication problems as well as the promise of much lower production costs.

Fig. 5.1, a 1964 design, shows that the sandwich type construction was retained and still presents a production problem, as no fewer than five components, three of them complex

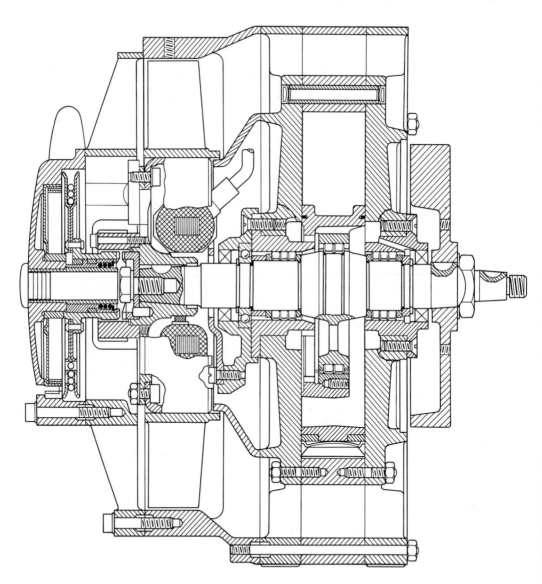

*Fig. 5.1. The simplification resulting from Dr. Ing. W. Froede's epoch-making inversion is even more apparent from these sectional illustrations of a fairly recent completely air cooled NSU/Wankel RC engine. This engine displaces 215 cm³ shaft revolution and develops 12 b.h.p. at 5,000 rev/min*

castings which, in addition, have to cope with combustion pressure and temperatures, must be kept in sufficiently accurate alignment so as to provide satisfactory bearing support for the output shaft. For a single rotor engine no fewer than five components must be kept in adequate alignment, and two more have to be added for every rotor of the multi-rotor engines. Several strippings and re-assemblies of the engine must be possible without sacrificing alignment and thereby jeopardising performance and reliability. Large diameter dowels have proved satisfactory to date, nevertheless there is undoubtedly scope for improvement which should facilitate a higher degree of interchangeability. The problem of alignment, real though it may be to production engineers, has never hampered the NSU/Wankel project, nor is it a problem exclusively peculiar to the Wankel RC engine.

Rotor and housing of the RC engine shown in Fig. 5.1 are air cooled, rotor cooling relying upon the incoming mixture, to which a small amount of oil — up to one part of oil for every hundred parts of fuel — is added for lubrication purposes. The housing assembly, which includes the end covers, depends for satisfactory cooling upon the axial

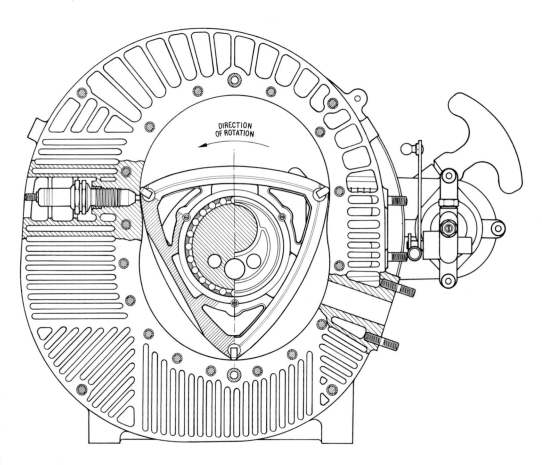

DIRECTION
OF ROTATION

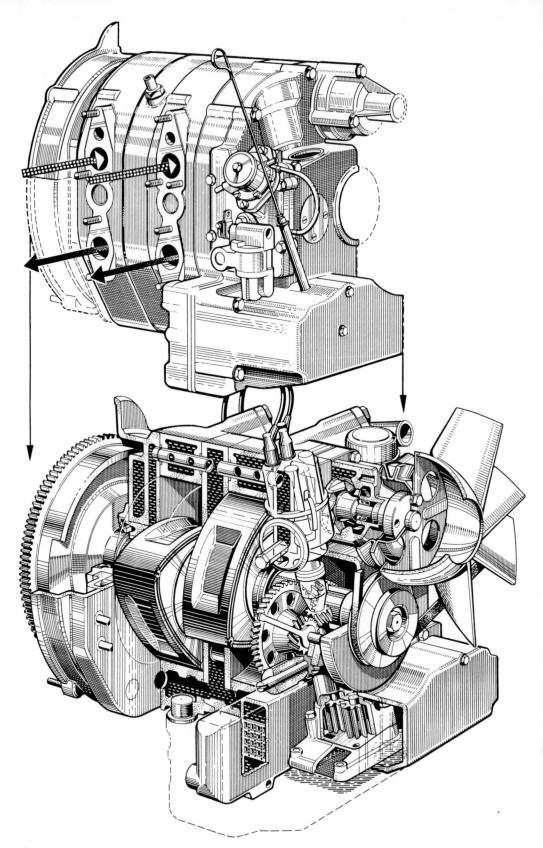

*Fig. 5.2. Twin rotor KKM 512 NSU/Wankel RC engine, which develops 110 b.h.p. at 6,000 rev/min. The housings are water cooled whereas the two rotors are oil cooled. It should be noted that the oil-cooler is conveniently accommodated in the sump*

flow fan, which is mounted co-axially with the generator, distributor and the rope and pulley type hand starting arrangement. Special weights attached to the fan hub, assisted by the asymmetrical flywheel at the output end of the shaft, are provided to balance the mass of the eccentric portion of the shaft and the rotor assembly.

In contrast, the twin rotor KKM 512 engine shown in Fig. 5.2 is a liquid cooled engine whose rotors are oil cooled, whilst the housing assembly is water cooled. Experience has shown that this arrangement facilitates the attainment of the highest b.m.e.p. figures. An empirical relationship seems to exist between the cooling method, inlet porting and b.m.e.p. as follows:

Table 5.1

| Cooling Medium | | Maximum b.m.e.p. % |
|---|---|---|
| Casing | Rotor | |
| Water | Oil—peripheral inlet port | 100 |
| Water | Oil—side inlet port | 85 |
| Air | Oil—peripheral inlet port | 90 |
| Water | Air (Mixture) | 75 |
| Air | Air (Mixture) | 60 |

Relying upon the mixture to cool the rotor en route to the working chamber increases its temperature, thereby reducing volumetric efficiency and consequently maximum power output, as shown in Table 5.1. This is not unexpected since the operating conditions of completely air cooled RC engines are in many respects similar to those prevailing in two-stroke reciprocating piston engines.

Although the *modus operandi* of the Wankel RC engine is already widely known, it would appear opportune to elaborate it further to prevent any doubts or confusion.

As indicated on p. 1, the Wankel RC engine works according to the Otto-cycle principle, the term four-stroke being only a correct definition of this cycle when applied to a reciprocating piston engine, hence there are four distinctly separate individual phases – induction, compression, expansion (actual working phase) and exhaust. The actual beginning and end of the respective phases may be blurred by overlapping port opening periods, but this is no more significant than the overlapping valve opening periods of reciprocating piston engines.

According to Fig. 5.3 a change from minimum to maximum chamber volume can only take place when the rotor turns through 90°; that is whilst a rotor flank moves from position $AB$ to $A'B'$, the contained volume increases gradually and induction occurs. During succeeding 90° rotor movements the compression, expansion and exhaust phases will take place in strict sequence as indicated in Fig. 5.4. To be precise, one complete thermodynamic cycle will take place in every one of the three chambers whilst the rotor turns through 360°. *It is this feature which has led many superficial observers to assert that a single rotor NSU/Wankel RC engine is 'of course' the equivalent of a three cylinder four-stroke engine. Why this is a fallacious belief will be explained in Chapter 6.*

Derivation of the epitrochoid by the method shown in Fig. 3.3 suggests that the shaft must make three complete revolutions for every single turn of the rotor, that is every

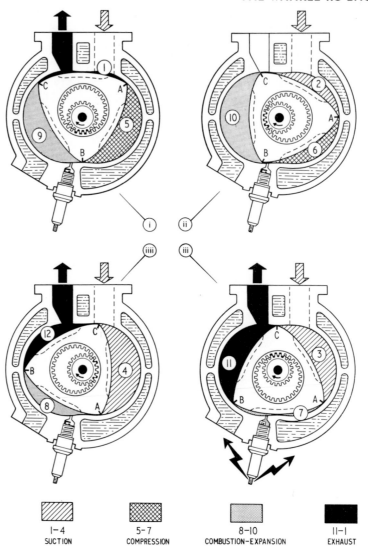

|   1–4   |   5–7   |   8–10   |   11–1   |
|:-------:|:-------:|:--------:|:--------:|
| SUCTION | COMPRESSION | COMBUSTION–EXPANSION | EXHAUST |

*Fig. 5.3.   1–4 induction*
*5–7 compression*
*8–10 expansion*
*11–1 exhaust*

thermodynamic phase extends over 270° of shaft rotation. It may be easier to appreciate this by looking at the position of the eccentric centre, which coincides with the c.g. and geometric centre of the rotor, on the minor axis relative to the output shaft centre *O*. As shown in Fig. 5.4 a rotor apex *C* can only be on the minor axis when the rotor centre is also on the minor axis, but on the opposite side of the output shaft centre *O*. Since the rotor has three apexes this condition occurs three times per rotor revolution, hence the shaft must turn three times as fast as the rotor. This is ensured by a ring gear which is attached to the rotor and a meshing spur pinion which is fixed to the appropriate end cover. It should be noted that the effective centre distance of these gears must be equal to $e$, the shaft eccentricity. The correct phasing is assured if the ring gear has 50% more teeth than the spur pinion, i.e. if the gear ratio is 2:3. According to theory or under ideal conditions no forces are imposed on these gears. However, one or two isolated failures demand explanation. Inertia and the friction between the rotor and eccentric

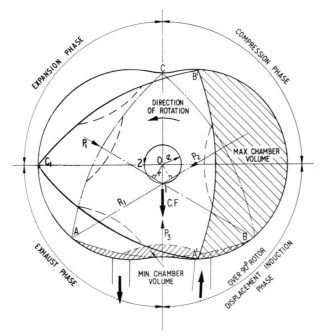

*Fig. 5.4. Thermodynamic phases relative to rotor movement are shown. For the chamber volume to change from a minimum $A-B$ to a maximum $A'-B'$ the rotor must turn through $90°$ and the eccentric shaft from 1 to 2, that is through $270°$ Gas pressures acting on every rotor flank may be resolved into a single force, as for instance $P_1$ for rotor flanks $C-A$ which must act through the rotor centre. The easiest way of finding the resultant force tending to turn the eccentric shaft at any specific position is by drawing a vector diagram representing the forces $P_1$ $P_2$ and $P_3$ as well as the centrifugal force of the mass of the rotor and the eccentric portion of the output shaft. The resultant will represent the actual turning force in magnitude and direction*

shaft portion may tend to turn the rotor in a forward direction whereas friction drag due to the sealing devices tends to prevent rotation. Whichever of these forces impose a variable or cyclic load on the gears leading to failure, there is no doubt that the gas forces do not impose a load on the phasing gears.

It ought perhaps to be mentioned that whereas only one set of external phasing gears would be required for a multirotor SIM type RC engine, in the case of PLM designs a pair of phasing gears is required for every rotor, see Fig. 4.1, because the motion of every rotor must be synchronised with that of the shaft.

The first SIM type NSU/Wankel RC engine (1958) was designated KKM 125. It displaced 125 cm³ per shaft revolution and developed 27 b.h.p. at 10,000 (shaft) rev/min; it shared an identical sealing system, Fig. 4.3, with the original DKM 125 design. A sealing grid as now known was not incorporated until the KKM 125H was built in 1959.

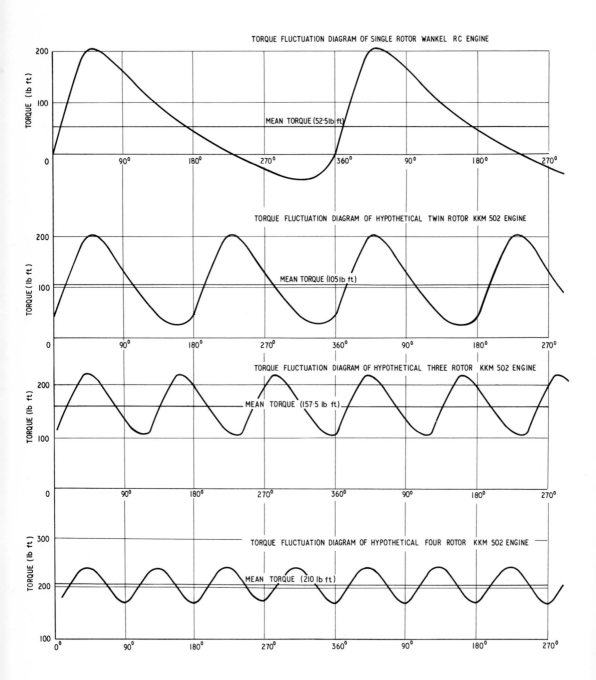

Fig. 5.5. *These torque fluctuation diagrams were derived from the indicator diagram of the NSU/KKM 502 RC engine see Fig. 12.1*

Compared to SIM type RC engines, the PLM configuration would seem to suffer from two disadvantages, high shaft stresses due to bending as well as torque, and the thermal demands made on the single ignition plug – possible benefits from multi-ignition have been investigated up to a point, and doubtless conclusive research will follow at a more opportune time. These two disadvantages appear insignificant when compared with the advantages of the PLM design.

Nevertheless, it can be said that in the absence of any reciprocating masses and valve actuating devices, the PLM Wankel RC engine appears to offer a potential for performance, speed and durability far in advance of that attainable by the reciprocating piston engine.

Larger and more powerful engines may be obtained by increasing the proportions of RC engines, by multiplying the number of rotors or by a combination of both methods. Despite apparent differences, as for instance the frequency of working phases making the single rotor Wankel RC engine the equivalent of a twin cylinder reciprocating piston engine, the reasons influencing the choice of proportions and/or the number of rotors remains, of course, the same for both types of engines. Smooth performance will be associated with minimum torque fluctuations and therefore with multi-rotor engines, as shown in Fig. 5.5.

Although this is not the place to discuss octane requirements of the NSU/Wankel RC engine, it should be emphasised that larger chamber size demands fuel with a higher octane rating, a phenomenon which is already known from the reciprocating piston engine field. Furthermore, a given engine size will be more tolerant of fuel with a lower octane rating than a reciprocating piston engine which has the same compression ratio. A great deal more research will be required before the full significance of this aspect is fully appreciated. At present Wankel RC type engines with compression ratios of 8–9·6 to 1 run satisfactorily on standard grade fuel, and a small 250 cm$^3$ single rotor experimental engine with a compression ratio of 8 to 1 has accepted fuel, without any audible protests, which has a rating of only 30.

The power output of a given RC engine can also be increased by supercharging: preliminary investigations at Curtiss-Wright have shown that 6 inHg supercharging pressure results in 30% more power.

# 6

# Fundamental Relationships of Wankel RC Engines

## 6.1. Fundamental Relationships

Performance of Wankel type RC engines depends as much upon certain fundamental proportions and mechanical relationships as that of any other type of engine. Some of these relationships may be obscure or more complex, as for instance the interdependence of thermal efficiency, compression ratio and the angle of obliquity $\phi$. This angle is variously called the angle of inclination or leaning angle. It is meant to define the maximum angle contained by the radial lines from the rotor centre through each apex point and the normal to the epitrochoidal bore at the point of contact as shown in Fig. 3.5.

As already indicated in Fig. 3.5, the actual bore is a constant distance $a$ outside the true epitrochoid, the dimension $a$ was introduced to create a constantly shifting contact line between the apex seals and the bore to avoid radial movement of the apex seals and in the interest of durability and improved heat dissipation. The mathematical relationship between $R$, $e$ and $\phi$ is given by the formula

$$\sin \phi = 3 \frac{e}{R}$$

or, in more general terms by

$$\sin \phi = Z \frac{e}{R} \tag{6.1}$$

where $Z$ denotes the number of corners or contacts between the rotor and the respective bore or the number of chambers. The complications arise because $\phi$ has also determining effects on the highest possible compression ratio, Fig. 6.1, and on the surface/volume ratio at the instance when the minimum volume is contained between a single rotor flank and the requisite portion of the trochoidal bore, see Figs. 6.2–6.4. Considering the $\varepsilon_{id}$ curve, that is the ideal or maximum compression ratio curve, obtainable only without any depression in the rotor flanks, it appears that the most compact combustion

44

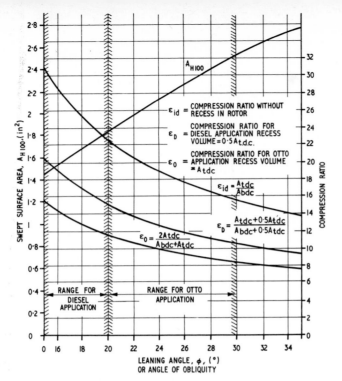

Fig. 6.1. Relationship between maximum angle of obliquity or leaning angle φ, swept surface area and maximum compression ratio respectively. Based on 2:3 epitrochoidal relationship and 100 mm length of the trochoid on the major axis

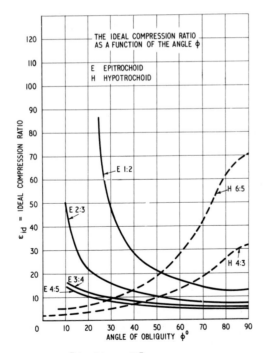

Fig. 6.2. Ideal compression ratio $\varepsilon_{id} = \dfrac{[A_s + (A_{min} - A_r)]}{A_{min} - A_r}$ (see Fig. 6.7) relative to angle of obliquity φ for various epitrochoidal and hypotrochoidal configurations

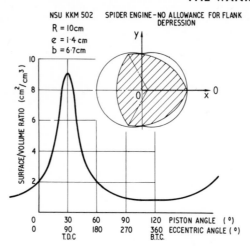

Fig. 6.3. (Taken from Appendix Fig. A.18)

chamber is obtainable at the lower values of $\phi$. Unfortunately this provides a rather long flat and thin combustion chamber with two slender 'tails' which could have detrimental effects on combustion under certain operating conditions.

The general relationship between the angle $\Phi$ and the 'Ideal' compression ratio (no depression in rotor flanks) for various epitrochoidal and hypotrochoidal engines is shown in Fig. 6.2. In practice it may be found more convenient to make use of the graph, Fig. 6.5, which was prepared by Ing. Kühner at F. Wankel's research establishment. The areas referred to are those between a rotor flank and the epitrochoidal bore, as shown on the drawing. To obtain the relevant volumes it is merely necessary to multiply the values obtained by the axial rotor length $B$, or more correctly by the axial width of the centre housing or chamber ($B_c$).

For simplicity's sake these curves are based on a fixed eccentricity $e_o = 1$ cm so that figures pertaining to other eccentricities can be obtained merely by multiplying the values

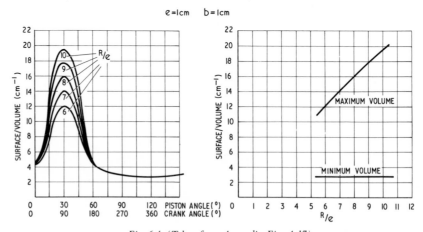

Fig. 6.4. (Taken from Appendix Fig. A.17)

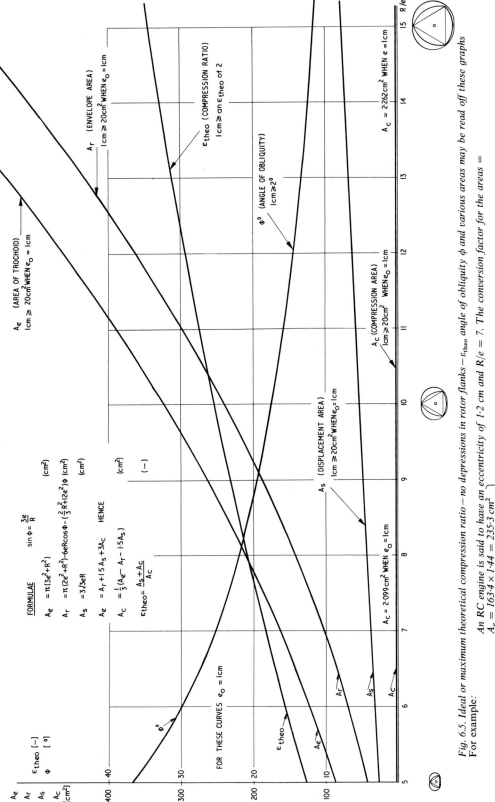

Fig. 6.5. Ideal or maximum theoretical compression ratio – no depressions in rotor flanks – $\varepsilon_{theo}$ angle of obliquity $\phi$ and various areas may be read off these graphs
For example:

An RC engine is said to have an eccentricity of $1.2$ cm and $R/e = 7$. The conversion factor for the areas =

$A_e = 163.4 \times 1.44 = 235.3\ cm^2$
$A_r = 102.36 \times 1.44 = 147.4\ cm^2$ ⎫ For significance of these areas see Fig. 6.7
$A_s = 36.375 \times 1.44 = 52.37\ cm^2$ ⎬
$A_c = 2.097 \times 1.44 = 3.02\ cm^2$ ⎭
$\phi = 25.35°$ ⎫ Read directly off graph
$\varepsilon_{theo} = 18.26$ ⎭

read off the respective graph, above the requisite $R/e$ ratio, with the conversion factor $(e/e_o)^2$. $e$ is the actual eccentricity of the proposed design and $e_o = 1$ cm. With regard to the angle of obliquity $\phi$, the values are read directly off the graph.

## 6.2. Calculation of displacement volume suggested by G. B. Sewards

To derive formulae from first principles for the calculation of the displacement volume of a single chamber proceed as follows:

As shown in Fig. 3.2 and given that the base circle radius = two rolling circle radii, the position of any point $P$ is defined by rectangular co-ordinates

$$\left.\begin{array}{l} x = R\cos\alpha - e\cos 3\alpha \\ y = R\sin\alpha - e\sin 3\alpha \end{array}\right\} \tag{6.2}$$

where $R = OC = 3 \times$ rolling circle radius or, dividing the expressions by $R$

$$\left.\begin{array}{l} \dfrac{1}{R}x = \cos\alpha - \dfrac{e}{R}\cos 3\alpha \\[2mm] \dfrac{1}{R}y = \sin\alpha - \dfrac{e}{R}\sin 3\alpha \end{array}\right\} \tag{6.3}$$

According to Fig. 3.5 all three apexes $P$, $Q$ and $S$ of the equilateral rotor lie on the epitrochoidal curve. Points $P$ and $Q$ in Fig. 6.6 are located by the angles $\alpha$ and $\alpha + \frac{2\pi}{3}$ respectively.

Hence (the area contained by the straight lines $OP$, $OQ$ and the epitrochoidal bore) − (the area of triangle $OPQ$) =

$$\int_{(\alpha)}^{(\alpha+\frac{2\pi}{3})} \tfrac{1}{2}OG^2 d\theta - \Delta OPQ$$

where $\theta$ is the angle between $OG$ and the abscissa. If $OG = r$, then,

$$r^2 d\theta = (x^2 + y^2)\, d\left(\arctan\frac{y}{x}\right) = x\,dy - y\,dx$$

$$= R^2 \left[\left[1 + 3\left(\frac{e}{R}\right)^2\right] - 4\left(\frac{e}{R}\right)\cos 2\alpha\right] d\alpha$$

Therefore $\displaystyle\int_{\alpha}^{\alpha+\frac{2\pi}{3}} \tfrac{1}{2}OG^2 d\theta = R^2\left[1 + 3\left(\frac{e}{R}\right)^2\right]\frac{\pi}{3} - eR\sqrt{3}\cos\left(2\alpha + \frac{2\pi}{3}\right)$

and the area of the triangle $OPQ = \frac{1}{2}PQ \times (\perp$ distance of $PQ$ from $O$). $PQ$ is obviously $\sqrt{3}R$, and the equation of $PQ$ is:

$$y - y(\alpha) + \cot\left(\alpha + \frac{\pi}{3}\right)[x - x(\alpha)] = 0 \tag{6.4}$$

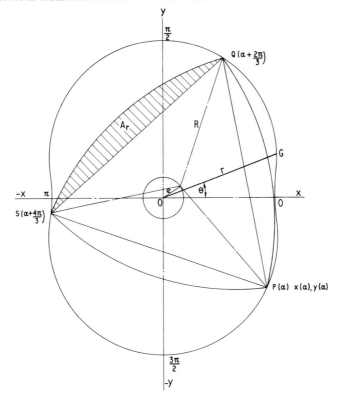

Fig. 6.6.

where $y(\alpha)$ and $x(\alpha)$ are taken from Fig. 6.6.
The perpendicular distance of $PQ$ from $O$ is, therefore,

$$\frac{y(\alpha)+x(\alpha)\cot\left(\alpha+\frac{\pi}{3}\right)}{\operatorname{cosec}\left(\alpha+\frac{\pi}{3}\right)}$$

which simplifies to $\dfrac{R}{2}-e\cos\left(2\alpha-\dfrac{\pi}{3}\right)$ (6.5)

and the area of the triangle $OPQ = \dfrac{\sqrt{3}}{2}\left[\tfrac{1}{2}-\dfrac{e}{R}\cos\left(2\alpha-\dfrac{\pi}{3}\right)\right]R^2$ (6.6)

and the area between the straight line $PQ$ and the epitrochoidal bore

$$= R^2\left[1+3\left(\frac{e}{R}\right)^2\right]\frac{\pi}{3}-eR\sqrt{3}\cos\left(2\alpha+\frac{2\pi}{3}\right)-\frac{\sqrt{3}R^2}{4}+\frac{\sqrt{3}}{2}eR\cos\left(2\alpha-\frac{\pi}{3}\right)$$ (6.7)

but $\cos\left(2\alpha-\dfrac{\pi}{3}\right) = -\cos\left(2\alpha+\dfrac{2\pi}{3}\right)$

therefore Equation 6.7 simplifies to

$$R^2 \left[ 1 + 3\left(\frac{e}{R}\right)^2 \right] \frac{\pi}{3} - \frac{\sqrt{3}R^2}{4} - \frac{3\sqrt{3}}{2} \cdot eR \cos 2\left(\alpha + \frac{\pi}{3}\right) \tag{6.8}$$

$$= \left[ R^2 + 3e^2 \right] \frac{\pi}{3} - \frac{\sqrt{3}R^2}{4} - \frac{3\sqrt{3}}{2} Re \cos 2\left(\alpha + \frac{\pi}{3}\right) \tag{6.9}$$

which has a minimum value when $\alpha = -60°$ and a maximum value when $\alpha = 30°$.

$$A_{min} = (R^2 + 3e^2)\frac{\pi}{3} - \frac{\sqrt{3}R^2}{4} - \frac{3\sqrt{3}}{2} eR \tag{6.10}$$

$$A_{max} = (R^2 + 3e^2)\frac{\pi}{3} - \frac{\sqrt{3}R^2}{4} + \frac{3\sqrt{3}}{2} eR \tag{6.11}$$

Therefore $A_{max} - A_{min} = A_s = +3\sqrt{3}\, eR$ \tag{6.12}

and the swept or displacement volume $V_s = 3\sqrt{3}R_1 B_c e$ \tag{6.13}

where $B_c$ is the axial length of the chamber and $R_1 = (R+a)$

In general terms, when we are dealing with a configuration which has $Z$ number of chambers

$$V_s = eR_1 B_c \frac{4Z}{Z-1} \sin\frac{\pi}{Z}$$

Furthermore, it is obvious from Fig. 6.7a that the area $A_r$ between the side bc of the equilateral triangle and the actual rotor flank contour can be totally disregarded for the determination of the displacement or swept volume. However, if the maximum theoretical compression ratio has to be found it is easiest to find the area $A_r$ between any rotor flank a–b and a side of the equilateral triangle abc with the aid of a planimeter.

Richard Vogel at the Technische Hochschule, Stuttgart, has evolved a formula whereby the whole area contained by the rotor flanks $ZA_R$ of any trochoidal rotor (the rotor contour being derived from an epitrochoidal bore) simplifies to the expression

$$ZA_R = \left[ \pi(R^2 + 2e^2) - 6eR \cos\phi - \left(\frac{2R^2}{Z} + 4Ze^2\right)\phi \right] \tag{6.14}$$

where $Z$ = the number of chambers or apexes in contact with the bore (see Equation 6.1
       = 3 for the familiar Wankel 2:3 configuration, so that Equation 6.14 reads

$$3A_R = \left[ \pi(R^2 + 2e^2) - 6eR \cos\phi - \left(\frac{2R^2}{3} + 12e^2\right)\phi \right] \tag{6.15}$$

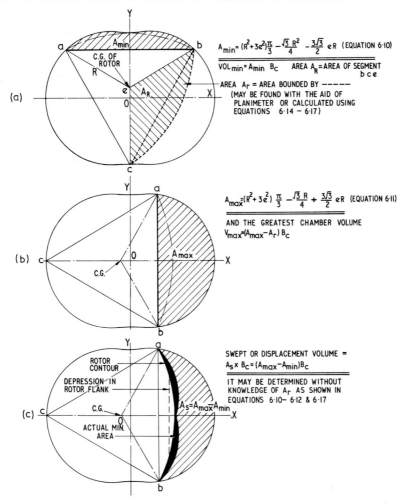

Fig. 6.7. These diagrams illustrate the relevant areas which must be determined if the displacement volume (per shaft revolution) and the compression ratio are to be calculated. The mathematics are obviously more involved than for the familiar reciprocating piston engine, though a great deal depends on the actual combustion chamber shape as well as upon the shape of the piston dome

$A_R$ is the area of one sector of the rotor, and the area of the triangle with $R_1$ as the length of two sides and an included angle of $\left(\dfrac{Z-1}{Z}\right)\pi$

$$= R_1 \times \frac{R_1}{2}\frac{\sqrt{3}}{2} = \frac{\sqrt{3}R_1^2}{4} \qquad (6.16)$$

so that $A_r = A_R - \dfrac{\sqrt{3}R_1^2}{4}$ \qquad\qquad (6.17)

and $\sin\phi = \dfrac{Ze}{R}$

## 6.3. Calculation of Compression Ratio

Assuming no depression in the rotor flanks, it is now possible to calculate the maximum theoretical compression ratio attainable with any engine configuration; to obtain the actual compression ratio it will be necessary to determine the volume of the depression in every rotor flank.

$$\text{Maximum theoretical compression ratio} = \text{Ratio of areas} = \frac{A_s + (A_{min} - A_r)}{A_{min} - A_r} \qquad (6.18)$$

If actual volumes are of interest it is, of course, necessary to multiply all the respective areas by the axial width of the chamber or centre casing $B_c$.

*It should be noted that Equations 6.10–6.17 are applicable when the bore is a true epitrochoid based upon the eccentricity and the generating radius R. The actual bore is, however, larger than the epitrochoid by a constant distance 'a'. Substituting in the formulae $R_1$ for R, the answers will be adequate for all practical purposes as the differences will only be marginal.*

*Example*

Given data for NSU/KKM 502 RC engine:

$$e = 1\cdot4 \text{ cm}$$
$$R = 10\cdot0 \text{ cm}$$
$$a = 0\cdot2 \text{ cm} \qquad \text{Therefore } R_1 = 10\cdot2 \text{ cm}$$
$$B_c = 6\cdot7 \text{ cm}$$
$$\phi = 24°19'; \sin\phi = \frac{Z \times e}{R_1} = \frac{3 \times 1\cdot4}{10\cdot2} = 0\cdot41176, \cos\phi = 0\cdot91152$$

$$\phi = 0\cdot42440$$

According to Equation 6.10 (see Fig. 3.2)

$$A_{min} = (R_1^2 + 3e^2)\frac{\pi}{3} - \frac{\sqrt{3R_1^2}}{4} - \frac{3\sqrt{3}}{2}R_1e$$

$$= (10\cdot2^2 + 3 \times 1\cdot4^2)\frac{\pi}{3} - \frac{\sqrt{3 \times 10\cdot2^2}}{4} - \frac{3\sqrt{3}}{2}10\cdot2 \times 1\cdot4$$

$$= 32\cdot9544 \text{ cm}^2$$

Area contained by rotor flanks $3A_R$ is found with the aid of Equations 6.14–6.16.

$$3A_R = \pi(R_1^2 + 2e^2) - 6eR_1 \cos\phi - \left(\frac{2R_1^2}{3} + 12e^2\right)\phi$$

(Note. $R_1$ is used in place of R).

$$3A_R = (10\cdot2^2 + 2 \times 1\cdot4^2) - 6 \times 1\cdot4 \times 10\cdot2 \times 0\cdot91152 - (\tfrac{2}{3} \times 10\cdot2^2 + 12 \times 1\cdot4^2) \, 0\cdot42440$$
$$= 339\cdot13496 - 78\cdot09903 - 39\cdot41827$$
$$= 221\cdot61766 \text{ cm}^2$$

$$A_r = \frac{221\cdot61766}{3} - (\text{area of triangle})$$

$$= \frac{221 \cdot 61766}{3} - \frac{\sqrt{3R_1}}{2} \times \frac{R_1}{2}$$

$$= \frac{221 \cdot 61766}{3} - \frac{\sqrt{3} \times 10 \cdot 2^2}{4}$$

$$= 73 \cdot 87255 - 45 \cdot 05192 = 28 \cdot 82063 \text{ cm}^2$$

$$A_{min} - A_r = 32 \cdot 95445 - 28 \cdot 82063 = 4 \cdot 13382 \text{ cm}^2$$

Actual minimum volume $= 4 \cdot 13382 \times 6 \cdot 7 = 27 \cdot 56259 \text{ cm}^3$

$$A_s = \frac{497 \cdot 16117}{6 \cdot 7} = 74 \cdot 20316$$

Therefore maximum theoretical compression ratio

$$\varepsilon_{theo} = \frac{A_s + (A_{min} - A_r)}{A_{min} - A_r}$$

$$= \frac{74 \cdot 20316 + 4 \cdot 13382}{4 \cdot 13382} = 18 \cdot 95026$$

## 6.4. Displacement and equivalent displacement volumes

As even engineers have, from time to time, expressed widely differing ideas about the volumetric displacement of the Wankel RC engine, it seems opportune to examine the facts and circumstances to see whether a rational answer is possible. Before entering upon this analysis it ought to be reiterated that the displacement volume of any positive displacement engine has no direct bearing upon power output.

Let $p$ = m.e.p. (lb/in$^2$)           Force $= F = p \times A$ lb
    $D$ = bore diameter (in)                    $=$ pressure $\times$ area
    $A$ = effective piston area (in$^2$)
    $L$ = stroke (ft)
    $S$ = total distance travelled by piston in unit time (ft/min)
       = mean piston speed (ft/min)
    $N$ = crankshaft speed (rev/min)
    $n$ = number of cylinders
    $f$ = number of working (expansion) phases per crankshaft revolution.
       $= \frac{1}{2}$ for four-stroke engine
    $\eta$ = mechanical efficiency (%)

Hence b.h.p.   $= \dfrac{F \times S \times \text{Constant} \times \eta}{33,000}$

$$= \left( p \times \frac{\pi D^2}{4} \right) (2LN) \left( \frac{nf}{2 \times 33,000} \right) \eta$$

$$= \frac{pD^2 S \eta n}{168,069} \tag{6.19}$$

where $168,069 = \dfrac{16 \times 33,000}{\pi}$

According to Equation 6.19, the power output of any positive displacement engine is *the product of the applied force* ($p \times A$) *multiplied by the distance* ($S$) *travelled by the piston in unit time.* It may be convenient for various purposes, such as for rapid comparison of different engines, to rearrange Equation 6.19 so that it appears to contain the displacement volume, but this expedient cannot overrule the basic facts.

It seems most unwise and unsatisfactory to dismiss the controversy in this summary fashion, as engine size is of considerable interest to the designer who, after all, deals with dimensions and proportions. An analytical approach may, therefore, yield other convincing facts.

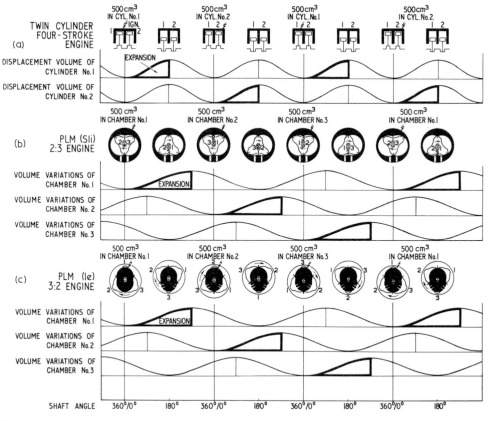

*Fig. 6.8 to 6.13. Comparison of the displacement volumes of various Otto-cycle reciprocating piston engines and RC engines relative to crankshaft or eccentric shaft rotation. Parts shown solidly black are stationary, those shown in outline only are the moving pistons or rotors*

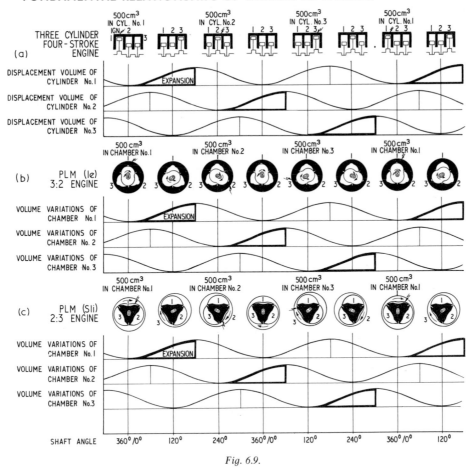

*Fig. 6.9.*

Engine performance is usually expressed as b.h.p. developed at crankshaft speed, the crankshaft being the first component capable of transmitting the forces exerted by one or more pistons to any other machine. Accordingly this may be considered as the definition of the *primary engine component.*

*Similarly the eccentric shaft of a Wankel RC engine is also a primary component as it is the first component capable of transmitting the forces acting on one or more rotors to any other machine.* It is, therefore, pertinent to plot or compare the volume displacement curves, which are sinusoidal for reciprocating and rotary piston engines, relative to crankshaft and eccentric shaft rotation respectively.

It is not disputed that a single cylinder two-stroke engine displaces nominally one stroke volume per crankshaft revolution so that it is, in fact, the equivalent of a four-stroke engine displacing twice as much, but the displacement per revolution is generally accepted. Various interpretations could be used to explain this anomaly, the most magnanimous explanation probably being that even scientists and engineers are not always consistent. In any case, the two-stroke engine as it is known today is most unlikely to

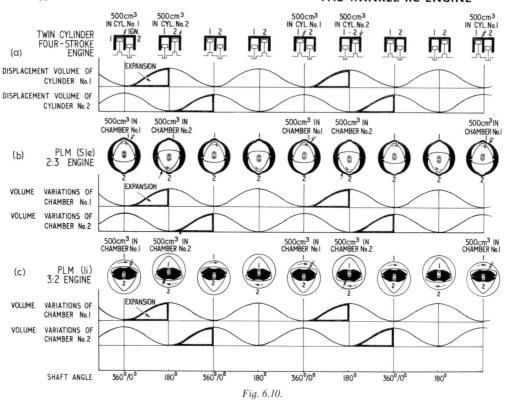

*Fig. 6.10.*

supersede the four-cycle engine in any major automotive application. It is therefore point-less to revive this particular controversy.

Fig. 6.8a shows the displacement curves of a parallel twin cylinder four-stroke engine, every phase extending nominally over 180° of crankshaft rotation and the actual working or expansion phases being outlined more heavily.

Fig. 6.8b shows the volume variation curves of a single rotor PLM (Sli) 2:3 engine, that is of a Wankel RC type engine. Clearly there are three curves as there are three vari-able volume chambers. The most notable feature is that every individual phase extends over 270° of shaft rotation – the shaft rotating at three times the speed of the rotor – so that no more than eight complete thermodynamic phases or two complete cycles occur during any two shaft revolutions. Consequently a single rotor Wankel RC engine is indeed the equivalent of a four-stroke twin cylinder reciprocating piston engine whose stroke volume of every piston equals the displacement volume of any flank of the Wankel RC engine.

Fig. 6.8c shows the volume variation curves of a so-called PLM(Ie)3:2 RC engine in which the inner rotor is stationary whilst the outer enveloping rotor moves in the manner of a planetary pinion by rotating about its own centre of gravity and simultaneously orbiting round the output shaft centre. As the sealing elements and curve generating points are accommodated in the outer and power transmitting component, it is the inner rotor which has the epitrochoidal shape. This engine also has three variable volume chambers and only two complete thermodynamic cycles occur during any two shaft revolutions.

Inverting the design of Fig. 6.8b and c by arranging that the rotors of the configurations shown in Fig. 6.8 are stationary and that the components which were stationary become the working rotors, we obtain the PLM(Ie)3:2 Fig. 6.9b and PLM(Sli)2:3 Fig. 6.9c. Assuming that the respective proportions have remained unaltered, it is evident from the volume variation curves that these two rotary piston engines are without doubt the equivalent of the three cylinder four-stroke engine shown in Fig. 6.9a.

It is emphasised that in proportion and superficially Fig. 6.8b would appear to be the same as Fig. 6.9c and Fig. 6.8c the same as Fig. 6.9b. All four engines have, in fact, three variable volume chambers.

Evidently this comparison underlines the importance of a careful analytical approach to RC engines, as mere counting of chambers will certainly fail to yield the correct answer as underlined by Figs. 6.10–6.13.

Fig. 6.10 and Fig. 6.11 depict RC engines which have ostensibly only two variable volume chambers, yet (as illustrated by the volume variation curves) these engines can also be the equivalent of either twin or three cylinder engines. Even so it is most unlikely

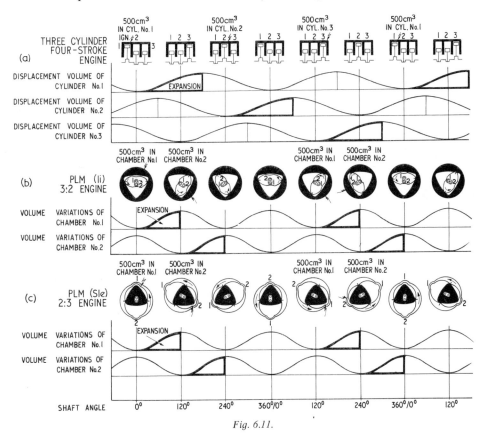

*Fig. 6.11.*

that any of the engines shown in Fig. 6.10 or in Fig. 6.11b and c will be produced without compelling reasons unconnected with engine design or performance. Consideration of torque and vibration characteristics suggests a different timing of the respective cycles; unfortunately it is impossible to arrange that the RC engines illustrated in Figs. 6.11 and 6.13 have their expansion phases equally spaced. However, they complete six thermodynamic cycles in four shaft revolutions which permits the conclusion that they are, for practical purposes, the equivalent of the three cylinder engines shown.

The RC engines shown in Fig. 6.12 and Fig. 6.13 are so-called single rotation engines,

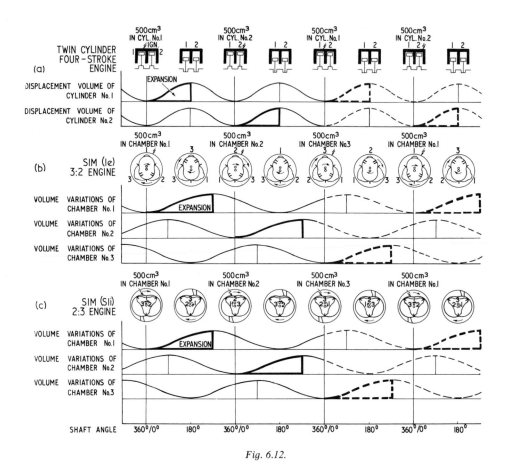

Fig. 6.12.

which means, according to Felix Wankel's book 'Rotary Piston Machines', that the two chambers forming components of the respective configurations rotate about their own centres of gravity.

Ing. D. Eiermann and Ing. H. Kühner, who work in close association with Felix Wankel, have evolved the general formulae for calculating rapidly the true equivalent maximum volume of RC engines possessing any convenient number of working chambers round a single rotor. They point out that non-intersecting trochoids and their complementary

rotors form variable volume chambers. It is immaterial whether these engines are classified as single (SIM) or planetary (PLM) rotation configurations, the respective maximum
and minimum volumes will be identical provided $\phi$, $e$, $R$ and $B_c$ of these engines are the
same for every design. Moreover, these volumes will be the same for hypotrochoidal and
epitrochoidal designs irrespective of their mode of engagement or the position of their
trochoid generating points, that is irrespective of whether they are to be denoted ($\overline{Sli}$),
($\overline{Sle}$), ($\overline{Ii}$) or ($\overline{Ie}$) machines. (For precise definitions of these notations see 'Rotary Piston
Machines').

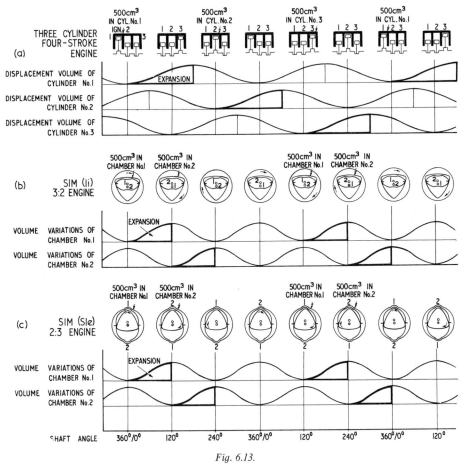

*Fig. 6.13.*

One method of finding maximum chamber volumes ($V_{max}$) has already been evolved,
nevertheless it may be pertinent to re-examine the conditions and see whether a different
approach yields the same results. Stroke × bore cross-sectional area signifies the displacement volume of reciprocating piston engines, and the maximum cylinder volume
($V_{max}$) is the stroke volume plus the volume contained by the piston and the cylinder head
when the piston is in the t.d.c. position. The position is very similar in RC engines except
that it is not always so obvious which are the relevant areas and which is the distance to

be taken into account. With reference to Fig. 6.7, the relevant area is represented by any side of the equilateral triangle abc which connects the apexes of the rotor, this area is

$$2(R_1 \sin \pi/3)B_c$$

for the familiar Wankel configuration, or in general terms it is

$$2 \left( R_1 \sin \frac{\pi}{Z} \right) B_c \qquad (6.20)$$

and the greatest chamber volume

$$V = (A_s + A_{min} - A_r)B_c = 2 \left( R_1 \sin \frac{\pi}{Z} \right) B_c \times (\text{Distance moved by this area})$$

The relevant distance is found as follows:

Assuming a rotor with $Z$ flanks and a stationary trochoid. The eccentric shaft of this configuration must make $Z$ complete revolutions for every single revolution of the rotor. One rotor flank covers $2(Z-1)$ working distances during every rotor revolution. When, therefore, the eccentric shaft turns through an angle $\alpha$ during one working phase

$$\alpha^c = \frac{Z \times 2\pi}{2(Z-1)} = \frac{Z \times \pi}{Z-1} \qquad (6.21)$$

The working distance is, of course, the distance covered by the centre of area of the flank perpendicular to the straight side connecting two apexes and any pressure on the rotor flank may be resolved into a force which acts through the centre of area at a variable radius $r$ about the output shaft centre.

$$\int dS = \int r \cdot d\alpha \quad \text{and} \quad r = e \sin \frac{Z-1}{Z} \alpha$$

the applicable limits for the integral are

$$\alpha_1 = 0 \text{ to } \alpha_2 = \frac{Z \times \pi}{Z-1}$$

$$\text{working distance } S = e \int_{\alpha_1 = 0}^{\alpha_2 = \frac{Z \times \pi}{Z-1}} \sin \frac{Z-1}{Z} \alpha \cdot d\alpha$$

$$= \left[ -e \frac{Z}{Z-1} \cos \left( \frac{Z-1}{Z} \right) \alpha \right]_{\alpha_1 = 0}^{\alpha_2 = \frac{Z \times \pi}{Z-1}}$$

$$= \frac{Z}{Z-1} e \left[ 1 - \cos \left( \frac{Z-1}{Z} \right) \left( \frac{Z \times \pi}{Z-1} \right) \right]$$

$$= e \frac{2Z}{Z-1}$$

so that

$$V = (A_s + A_{min} - A_r)B_c = R_1 e B_c \cdot \frac{4.Z}{Z-1} \sin \frac{\pi}{Z} \text{ cm}^3 \qquad (6.22)$$

This formula simplifies to

$$V = 3\sqrt{3} e R_1 B_c \qquad (6.23)$$

for the familiar Wankel configuration, where $Z = 3$ and $\sin \dfrac{\pi}{3} = \tfrac{1}{2}\sqrt{3}$.

(The above solution was worked out by Ing. H. Kühner and was first published in MTZ issue 3, March 1964, and reprinted as a leaflet for Technische Entwicklungs Stelle der Fraunhofer Gesellschaft E.V., Lindau.)

*Example*
The data of the NSU/Wankel KKM 502 engine as fitted to the NSU Spider car are:

$$e \ = \ 1\cdot 4 \text{ cm}$$
$$R \ = \ 10\cdot 0 \text{ cm}$$
$$a \ = \ 0\cdot 2 \text{ cm}$$
$$R_1 = 10\cdot 2 \text{ cm}$$
$$\phi \ = \ 24° \ 19'$$
$$B_c \ = \ 6\cdot 7 \text{ cm}$$

and disregarding the depression in the rotor flanks

$$V = (A_s + A_{min} - A_r)B_c = 3\sqrt{3} e R_1 B_c$$
$$= (A_{max} - A_{min})B_c$$

$$A_{max} = e^2 \pi - R_1^2 \frac{\sqrt{3}}{4} + R_1^2 \frac{\pi}{3} + e \cdot R_1 \frac{3\sqrt{3}}{2} \qquad \text{(from Equation 6.11)}$$

$$= 1\cdot 96\pi - 104\cdot 04 \frac{1\cdot 732}{4} + \frac{104\cdot 04\pi}{3} + 1\cdot 4 \times 10\cdot 2 \times \frac{3 \times 1\cdot 732}{2}$$

$$= 107\cdot 1576 \text{ cm}^2$$

$$A_{min} = e^2 \pi - R_1^2 \times \frac{\sqrt{3}}{4} + R_1^2 \frac{\pi}{3} - e R_1 \times \frac{3\sqrt{3}}{2} \qquad \text{(from Equation 6.10)}$$

$$= 32\cdot 95445 \text{ cm}^2$$
$$V = (107\cdot 1576 - 32\cdot 95445)6\cdot 7 = 497\cdot 16117 \text{ cm}^3$$
$$= 3\sqrt{3} e R_1 B_c \text{ (according to Equation 6.23)}$$
$$= 3 \times 1\cdot 732 \times 1\cdot 4 \times 10\cdot 2 \times 6\cdot 7 = 497\cdot 16117 \text{ cm}^3$$

## 6.5. Surface/Volume Ratio

The surface/volume ratio is often quoted as a relationship which allows conclusions about the interplay of the actual heat release during combustion and the proportions of the combustion chamber. Nevertheless it is doubtful whether it has much more than red herring value. Text books preserve a virtually ominous silence on this subject, and there is little controversy about it in professional automobile engineering circles.

By way of definition it may be assumed that by the surface/volume ratio is meant the relationship between the minimum volume within a cylinder when the piston is at the t.d.c. position and the relevant surface is the surface area of the chamber when the volume is at its minimum.

Assuming a fixed displacement volume, a hemispherical cylinder head matching up to a 76 mm diameter bore which contains a flat top piston. Considering compression ratios ($\varepsilon$) of 10 to 1 and 5 to 1, the surface/volume ratio for an $\varepsilon$ of 10 to 1 =

$$\frac{136 \cdot 09379}{114 \cdot 92424} = 1 \cdot 1842 \text{ cm}^{-1}$$

and when $\varepsilon$ is 5 to 1 the surface/volume ratio =

$$\frac{211 \cdot 70152}{258 \cdot 57965} = 0 \cdot 81870 \text{ cm}^{-1} = 100\%$$

$$\text{and } \frac{1 \cdot 1842}{0 \cdot 8187} = 144 \cdot 64\%$$

This means that high compression ratio engines have necessarily inferior surface/volume ratios which approach infinity towards the absolute limit.

Furthermore, it is imperative to state precisely the units used in calculating a particular surface/volume ratio. For example, the Surface/volume ratio of the above 76 mm diameter chamber for a compression ratio of 10 to 1 is, in metric units,

$$\frac{136 \cdot 09379}{114 \cdot 92424} = 1 \cdot 1842 \text{ cm}^{-1}$$

whilst in Imperial units – square and cubic inches respectively – it amounts to

$$\frac{136 \cdot 09379}{114 \cdot 92424} \times 2 \cdot 54 = 3 \cdot 008 \text{ in}^{-1}$$

Some of the factors which have a determining influence upon the significance of the surface/volume ratio are, for example:

1. The material of the chamber walls – cylinder head and piston.
2. The heat transfer capacity of the respective material.
3. The wall temperatures under operating conditions.
4. Factors 2 and 3 obviously alter as carbon deposits build up on the surface.
5. Chamber shape, turbulence, ignition timing, presence of an oil film etc.

Nor is it yet possible to incorporate the innumerable variables into some formula so that a computer could work out a valid comparative index figure.

Whilst throwing doubt on the significance of the surface/volume ratio, it is not intended to ridicule its consideration, but to suggest that it poses a most complex problem so that perfectly valid conclusions applicable to reciprocating piston engines cannot be applied simply because both types of engines rely upon the same thermodynamic cycle. Due to the different conception of the RC engine mechanism there are unavoidable differences in the internal gas velocities and different heat loss factors are applicable because the whole mass of the mixture is moved round. Recognition of these factors is important and indicates a point where certain research and development may start.

Perhaps it should be frankly admitted that not enough is known to date about the surface/volume relationship, even of the conventional reciprocating piston engine, to allow any conclusions, applicable to the reciprocating piston engine, to be presented as irrevocable criteria permitting a forecast concerning combustion phenomena in the Wankel RC engine. Of course, no engine designer will deliberately include seemingly undesirable features in his design, and this includes an unrealistic surface/volume relationship. In cases of doubt, as in this instance, special care is required in the design stages lest undesirable influences gain determining significance. This seems perfectly feasible in the case of the surface/volume ratio by arranging that neither hot spots nor local overcooling can occur. It should perhaps be emphasised that research into these aspects of performance has already permitted pin-pointing of certain parameters of the surface/volume relationship relative to performance; nevertheless, a great deal more research effort seems necessary before the significance of this relationship can be exhaustively interpreted for all circumstances and applications.

Those who may wish to look deeper into the problems associated with the surface/volume relationship are obliged to calculate the relevant bore areas and that of a rotor flank.

The length of the trochoidal bore when the minimum volume is contained between it and a rotor flank is found as follows, using Fig. 6.14.

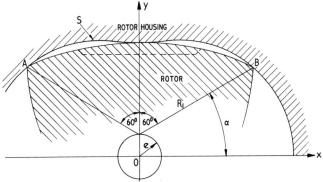

*Fig. 6.14. A fractionally less favourable surface/volume ratio is obtained by calculating S according to Equation 6.25 which seems adequate for most practical purposes since the value of the surface/volume ratio for comparative evaluation is suspect. Accurate results are obtainable by using Equations 3.3a and 3.4a. (Fig. 3.5) for the calculation of the rectangular co-ordinates of the requisite points on the curve and by altering Equations 6.24 and 6.25*

Length $s$ of locus of point $P$

$$x = e \cos 3\alpha + R_1 \cos \alpha$$
$$y = e \sin 3\alpha + R_1 \sin \alpha$$
$$dx = (-3e \sin 3\alpha - R_1 \sin \alpha)d\alpha$$
$$dy = (+3e \cos 3\alpha + R_1 \cos \alpha)d\alpha \qquad (6.24)$$
$$dx^2 = (9e^2 \sin^2 3\alpha + R^2 \sin^2\alpha + 6eR_1 \sin \alpha \sin 3\alpha)d\alpha^2$$
$$dy^2 = (9e^2 \cos^2 3\alpha + R^2 \cos^2\alpha + 6eR_1 \cos \alpha \cos 3\alpha)d\alpha^2$$
$$dx^2 + dy^2 = 9e^2 + R_1^2 + 6eR_1(\sin \alpha \sin 3\alpha + \cos \alpha \cos 3\alpha)d\alpha^2$$
$$= (9e^2 + R_1^2 + 6eR_1 \cos 2\alpha)d\alpha^2$$

since         $\sin \alpha \sin 3\alpha + \cos \alpha \cos 3\alpha = \cos 2\alpha = 1 - 2\sin^2\alpha$

$$\sin A \sin B + \cos A \cos B = \cos (A - B)$$
$$S = \int\sqrt{[9e^2 + R_1^2 + 6eR_1 \cos 2\alpha]}d\alpha \qquad (6.25)$$
$$= \int\sqrt{[9e^2 + R_1^2 + 6eR_1 - 12eR_1 \sin^2\alpha]}d\alpha$$
$$= \int(3e + R_1)\sqrt{(1 - k^2 \sin^2\alpha)}d\alpha$$

where  $k^2 = \dfrac{12eR_1}{(3e + R_1)^2}$

The answer is an elliptical integral of the second order. If $e$ and $R_1$ are known it may be worked out with the assistance of tables of elliptical integrals.

Since the rotor flank contour is derived from the actual bore, that is it is generated by a curve parallel to a true epitrochoid, it seems unjustified to exert considerable mathematical effort in order to find the actual area of a rotor flank, especially if the indispensable depression in every flank is taken into account. Direct measurement of the length of this flank by any convenient means seems adequate, alternatively it is possible to draw a radius which approximately coincides with the rotor contour and calculate the length of the arc.

According to Fig. 6.15         $\sin \theta = \dfrac{R_1 \sin \dfrac{\pi}{3}}{R_o}$

where $R_o$ is the radius of the equivalent circular arc and $\theta$ is half the subtended angle.

Therefore, the length of arc $= \int = \dfrac{R_o(2\theta)\pi}{180}$

and the approximate flank area (disregarding the depression)

$$= \dfrac{R_o(2\theta)\pi}{180} B_c \qquad (6.26)$$

The shape of the depression will suggest the easiest method by which its surface area/volume may be calculated. Hence the surface volume/ratio $=$

$$\dfrac{S \cdot B_c + 2(A_{min} - A_r) + \dfrac{R \cdot (2\theta)\pi}{180} B_c \pm (\text{Area of Depression})^*}{(A_{min} - A_r)B_c + (\text{Volume of Depression})} \qquad (6.27)$$

*When calculating the surface area of the depression it must not be forgotton that the area of the depression, as projected onto the rotor contour, has already been included.

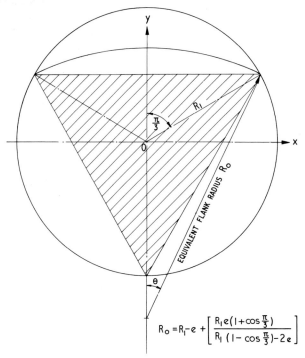

$$R_o = R_r - e + \left[ \frac{R_1 e (1 + \cos \frac{\pi}{3})}{R_1 (1 - \cos \frac{\pi}{3}) - 2e} \right]$$

*Fig. 6.15.*

Charles Jones, in charge of RC engine work at Curtiss Wright, wrote in his S.A.E. paper 886D in 1964:

'The study of RC engine combustion is still in its early stages. Nonetheless, it is apparent that a whole new set of comparative parameters will have to be developed specifically for this engine breed. For example, the over-simplification of the surface/volume ratio falls apart as a valid heat loss index because of the different internal gas velocities, metal temperature distributions, characteristic dimensions for film thickness, and radiation factors. Having mentioned the surface/volume ratio it would be appropriate to add that it is 7·2 for the RC-60, as compared to a range of roughly between 4·5 and 10 for current (American reciprocating piston) engines, with higher compression ratios and increasing bore-stroke ratios tending towards the high end.

Insofar as detonation, pre-ignition, rumble and similar phenomena are concerned, surveys covering a range of compression ratios, rotor combustion chamber configurations and different fuel ratings have indicated the RC engine to be generally similar to automotive engines in these respects'

Considerably more knowledge has accumulated since then but very little is, as yet, available for publication. However, high speed films of the combustion process have revealed that flame propagation is primarily downstream, that is in the direction of rotation. Fig. 6.16 is intended to illustrate this trend. Ionisation detection plugs have confirmed these findings.

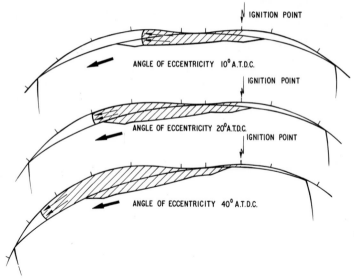

*Fig. 6.16. Flame propagation with standard symmetrical depression in rotor flank. Propagation is in direction of rotation only*

Dual ignition and reliance upon a plug in either the leading or trailing portion of the chamber can also affect combustion. Fig. 6.17 shows the more sudden rise in pressure and a slimmer expansion curve resulting from reliance upon dual ignition and consequential more rapid heat release. At 4,000 rev/min, combustion is about 3 msec whereas when a single plug is used it takes about 4 msec. The effects of dual ignition and ignition

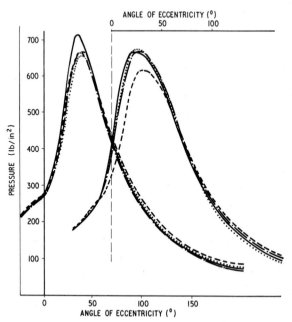

*Fig. 6.17. Comparison of the pressure-time variations of an NSU/Wankel RC engine at 5,000 rev/min running with a wide open throttle and firing a single plug and two plugs simultaneously*

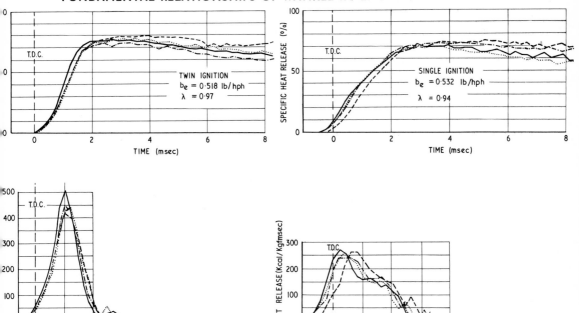

Fig. 6.18. Heat release and specific heat release of NSU/Wankel RC engine at 5,000 rev/min running with a wide-open throttle and firing a single plug and two plugs simultaneously

by a single plug in one of the two alternative positions is shown in Fig. 6.18. Similar results were obtained at 2,000 rev/min, when the heat energy release period was, of course, longer.

Considering the infinite variety of shapes for the depressions in the rotor flanks relative to various spark plug positions, not to mention any possible effects of fuel injection and temperature control of the rotor and the casing, it will be recognised that this may preoccupy research engineers for many years to come. Most important of all, these results suggest that there is greater flexibility in the way combustion may be influenced than there seems to be in reciprocating piston engines.

It would be presumptuous to speculate on the outcome of research into these very complex realms, though there is no reason to believe that the task cannot be accomplished by modern research facilities and techniques.

It is of interest to note the manner in which the surface/volume ratio of the Wankel RC engine varies as the rotor turns. D. J. Lockley, M.Sc., of The B.S.A. Group Research Centre has worked out these variations for the NSU KKM 502 engine, Fig. 6.3, as well as the fundamental relationship between the basic RC engine proportions given by $R/e$ and the surface/volume ratio, Fig. 6.4. These graphs emphasise the importance of extreme caution when comparing instantaneous or maximum surface/volume relationships.

# 7

# Sealing

Sealing Wankel RC engines presents, of course, entirely different problems from those encountered with the familiar reciprocating piston engine. Whatever these problems may be, they have been grossly exaggerated and even confused with wear and complex metallurgical and dynamic problems. For instance, bore wear in reciprocating piston engines may be minimised by the use of more suitable high temperature lubricants and/or better matching of cylinder bore surface and ring materials — hard chroming of the top end of the bore for example.

Sealing efficiency is, by comparison, perhaps more of a design function depending upon component production limits, which ought to be chosen so that there is practically no gap when the ring is fitted. In addition piston rings are expected to make continuous contact right round the bore and one side must make uninterrupted contact with the respective side of the groove which accommodates the ring.

It is necessary to differentiate between the gas sealing rings and the oil scraper ring. As the name implies, the sealing rings are intended to form a reasonably gas tight joint, to facilitate the attainment of the requisite compression ratio and to prevent hot gases issuing through the clearance between piston and bore into the crankcase. The oil scraper ring is to make sure 'ideally' that no more oil is left on the cylinder wall than is required to lubricate the sealing rings and to act as the sealing medium between the ring and the bore and a groove side respectively.

Conditions are somewhat different in completely air cooled Wankel RC engines, that is in engines where the casing as well as the rotor are air cooled — various experimental NSU designs and the Fichtel & Sachs KM 48 industrial engine. Their gas sealing problems are in some respects similar to those of two-stroke engines, as the mixture also contains the requisite amount of lubricating oil. In short they incorporate a total loss lubrication system, the mixture is passed through the rotor for cooling purposes and the oil is to lubricate the bearings and the gas sealing system.

## 7.1. The Oil Sealing Arrangement

Completely liquid cooled engines – NSU Spider KKM 502 or KKM 512 (Fig. 5.2) incorporate a second sealing system designed to prevent uncontrolled leakage losses. Air and liquid cooled engines can, and do, rely upon identical gas sealing arrangements, whilst an additional oil (or water) sealing system must be provided for liquid cooled rotors.

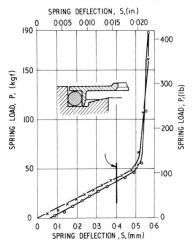

Fig. 7.1. Early diaphragm type coolant oil-seal of rotor (NSU configuration)

An early diaphragm face type oil-seal, Fig. 7.1, presented manufacturing problems; furthermore, it was not easy to ensure adequate sealing contact between the sealing edge and the side cover under all operating conditions and at acceptable pressures. The problem was, as for all face type seals, to provide a sufficiently flat side cover and/or an adequately flexible sealing element capable of maintaining contact at all speeds with the respective side cover – which may have distorted under the influence of temperature and pressure.

Later sealing arrangements are shown in Fig. 7.2, and Fig. 7.3 relate oil and friction losses to shaft speed, and thereby suggests that these sealing systems may have far-reaching effects on engine performance and efficiency, and could cause unsatisfactory exhaust emission.

Piston ring type sealing arrangements have, of course, been used before on turbines and at the output end of racing car engine crankshafts. Nevertheless, Fig. 7.2b shows perhaps a far more sophisticated design as a relief valve was incorporated to control the gas pressure in the space between the sealing elements to about 5 lb/in², thereby ensuring satisfactory contact of all primary and secondary sealing areas, the implications of which will be explained in the part dealing with the detail design of the gas sealing system.

Figs. 7.3a and b which indicate oil and friction losses due to the sealing arrangement may be considered an interpretation of sealing efficiency; they were presented by Dr. Ing. Walter Froede in his James Clayton Lecture of February 1966. He stressed that 'it may

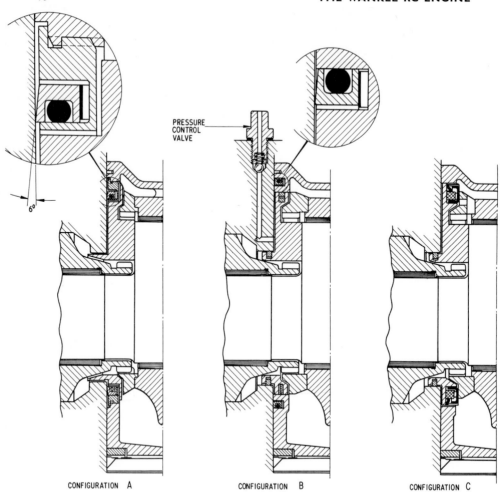

PRESSURE
CONTROL
VALVE

60°

CONFIGURATION  A          CONFIGURATION  B          CONFIGURATION  C

*Fig. 7.2. Various later oil-seal arrangements; configuration B is preferred*

be of interest to mention that the maximum permitted speed of the engine to date is limited by two factors: *oil consumption* and the *life of spark plugs*.'

## 7.2. Gas Sealing

By way of definition it may be said that piston rings and the sealing devices of Wankel RC engines are provided to block the escape of gas and/or oil by way of the variable running clearances between the respective rotors and the chamber walls. These clearances vary due to the different expansion characteristics and temperatures of the respective components as pointed out on page 9. Failure to incorporate effective sealing devices in an engine made from conventional engineering materials such as steel, cast iron and

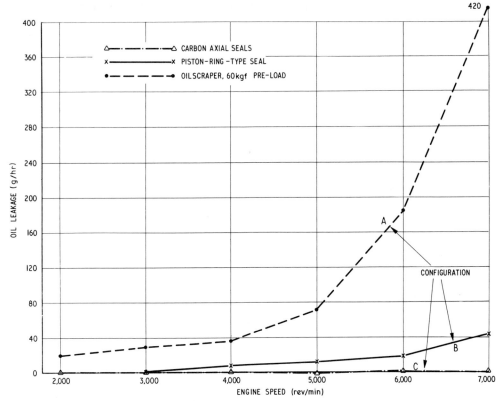

Fig. 7.3a. Oil leakages of different oil-seal arrangements designed for NSU/Wankel RC engines

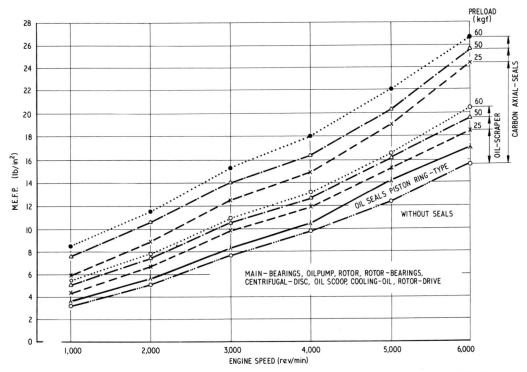

Fig. 7.3b. M.E.P. requirements to overcome the friction of various oil-seal arrangements designed for NSU/Wankel RC engines

aluminium results in starting difficulties, noise and excessive exhaust emission. Nor have any of the numerous and periodic claims by ambitious inventors proved the feasibility of running reciprocating piston engines without any form of piston rings. Nowadays it is normal to fit three rings, of which two perform sealing functions, whilst the third is the oil-scraper ring. More than three rings have and still may be used, and one specialist of high performance engines fits only a single ring to the pistons of some of his engines. Despite this last exception it may safely be concluded that a piston ring is perhaps a rather imperfect sealing element. It must, however, be pointed out that a piston ring is much more than a mere slotted ring machined from a piece of cast iron, indeed the manu-facturing process is intricate and its shape disguises its ability to fulfil its purpose over a very wide performance range for very extended periods, although the unavoidable split and the cylinder bore wear pattern as shown in Fig. 7.4 reduce ring effectiveness in time.

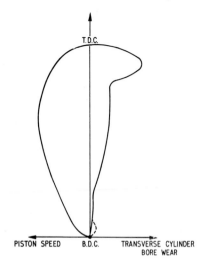

*Fig. 7.4. Relationship between piston speed and cylinder bore wear of a particular reciprocating piston engine. Only if dirty oil reaches the cylinder wall is there a slight increase in wear as the b.d.c. is approached*

In the Wankel RC engine the problems are of a different order from those of recipro-cating piston engines because at least some operating conditions differ considerably. It may, however, help to form a realistic appreciation of the issues involved by elaborating and comparing operating conditions and detail design features applicable to piston rings of the familiar reciprocating piston engine and of the seals of Wankel RC type engines.

There is no doubt that pistons and their rings come to complete rest momentarily at the end of every stroke, piston speed varies continuously and maximum piston speed occurs at the instant when the straight line between the gudgeon pin centre and the big end centre is normal (at 90°) to the line joining the crank throw centre with the crankshaft centre. Fig. 7.4 shows a typical piston speed diagram together with a characteristic cylinder bore wear pattern. It should be noted that in general terms cylinder bore wear is least where piston speed is high and where lubrication may be assumed to be excellent.

Piston rings have to perform a far more complex task than is suggested by the diagram because the bore wear pattern in the longitudinal plane of the crankshaft is different from the transverse pattern shown. In short, it is far from uniform. Therefore, piston rings would have to possess most extraordinary flexibility besides expending considerable energy if they are to maintain completely uninterrupted contact with the respective bore all along the stroke at all engine speeds especially if the rings alone had to perform the sealing function.

All efforts to produce engines without piston rings have so far proved unacceptable to the manufacturers.

Disregarding for a moment wear phenomena and the indispensable assistance rendered by the lubricating oil, it may be assumed that the rings make area contact with the bore, the primary sealing area and the side of the grooves, the secondary sealing areas containing them during the compression, expansion and probably during most of the exhaust stroke. Ring resilience, friction and gas pressure help to ensure this as far as possible.

Finally it may be pointed out that the potential leakage path of every cylinder consists approximately of the running clearance round the piston plus the circumferences of the effective valve seatings, it being reasonable to assume that the 'Static joint' between the cylinder head and block is gas tight for practical purposes. Similarly it may be assumed that the potential leakage path of, let us say, the NSU/Wankel KKM 502 engine is twice the axial running clearance between rotor and housing, times the length from the oil sealing ring to the apex contact point, plus the length of two apex seals. A different and much longer leakage path may exist in some air cooled engines where leakages into the inlet gases, passing through the rotor for cooling purposes, may be possible.

Evidently the disposition of sealing devices or their relative sizes do not necessarily determine the effective leakage path which, according to definition, is *the area controlling the escape of liquid or gas from any vessel, chamber or container.*

Assuming the valve of a liquid container is fully open, the critical area controlling the flow will be at the outlet end irrespective of the size and position of the valve. On closing the valve it is the uncovered valve port area which controls the flow from the moment that this effective area is smaller than the final outlet, that is if the shape of the two areas is disregarded. This principle applies to any sealing system however sophisticated and, therefore, it applies also to the sealing arrangement of Wankel RC engines. No valid or sensible conclusions can be derived from an addition and comparison of the length of the primary and secondary sealing areas of reciprocating piston and of equivalent single chamber Wankel RC engines, except that their lengths need not be numerically identical. If, for some reason, it is imperative to make a comparison it seems perfectly reasonable to check pressure drop in unit time or the leakage volume of a given liquid at a specified temperature and pressure. Rational arguments could also be found for advocating that sealing elements ought to be positioned at or close to the potential leakage path of such a complex mechanism as an RC engine. This is, in fact, the case in various air cooled Wankel RC engines as well as in those having side inlet ports where apex seals separate one chamber from those adjacent, and the side sealing elements, which contribute to this, primarily separate the gases within each respective chamber and those in the induction system and flowing through the rotor for cooling purposes.

Fig. 7.5 shows a much favoured sealing grid of a Wankel RC engine; although the grid is shown for the whole rotor and every apex seal is of equal importance to the two

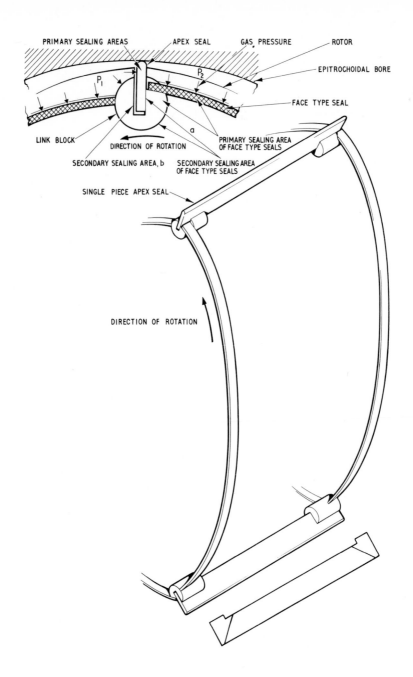

PRIMARY SEALING AREAS    APEX SEAL    GAS PRESSURE    ROTOR

$P_1$    $P_2$

EPITROCHOIDAL BORE

FACE TYPE SEAL

LINK BLOCK    a

DIRECTION OF ROTATION    PRIMARY SEALING AREA OF FACE TYPE SEALS

SECONDARY SEALING AREA, b    SECONDARY SEALING AREA OF FACE TYPE SEALS

SINGLE PIECE APEX SEAL

DIRECTION OF ROTATION

*Fig. 7.5a. One of the niceties of this Wankel RC engine sealing grid is that every apex seal and its associated link blocks are part of two adjacent and complete sealing grids. Some apex seals are in three parts as shown to ensure adequate sealing even after the end faces of the apex seals have worn*

chambers on either side of it, only two apex seals, two side sealing strips and four link blocks make up a complete sealing grid for every single chamber.

It was Dipl. Ing. Wolf Dieter Bensinger, who heads car engine design and development, including the RC engine project at Daimler Benz (Mercedes), who pointed out* *that a sealing grid of this nature can only perform its allocated task if all primary and secondary sealing areas are in uninterrupted contact.* The primary sealing areas are those between the components of the whole grid and the stationary housing—epitrochoidal bore and side covers—the sealing grid as a whole moving at rotor speed. The secondary sealing areas are those between the same components of the grid and the side of the grooves or bores accommodating them.

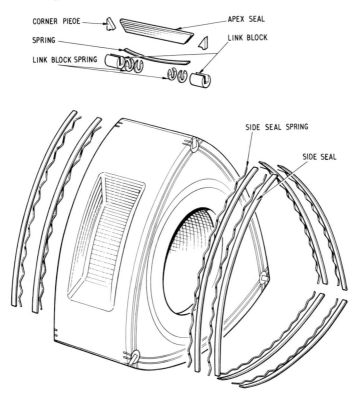

*Fig. 7.5b. This is a currently preferred sealing arrangement, double side seals were incorporated to improve sealing and facilitate easier interchangeability. By comparison with Fig. 7.5a this sealing grid must be described as 'incomplete' as not all leakage paths are blocked. It was found that this type of grid is satisfactory under operating conditions*

Having explained that the sealing grid can only be effective if primary and secondary sealing area contact is continuous, it should also be pointed out that this is somewhat misleading as metal to metal contact is unlikely to be achieved, nor can it in fact be maintained.

*BENSINGER, W. D., *ATZ*, **4**, April, 1964.

Furthermore, metal to metal contact is decidedly undesirable as it would produce excessive wear and high friction losses. The presence of sufficient lubricating oil improves sealing and at the same time reduces the tendency towards wear and friction losses. Despite the remarkably sophisticated conception and detail design of this sealing grid it is also necessary to make sure that adequate forces ensure satisfactory sealing contact regardless of possible unfavourable surface conditions and dynamic influences. This task is assigned to gas pressure, and adequate sealing for starting conditions is ensured by light springs behind every component of the sealing grid which ensures contact of the primary sealing surfaces.

In addition to these functional requirements the sealing grid (Fig. 7.5) must also be capable of accommodating manufacturing tolerances and differential thermal expansion of the sealing elements, the rotor and the housing.

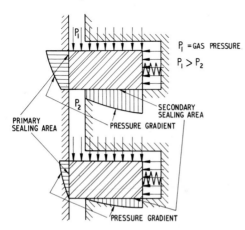

*Fig. 7.6. It is hardly necessary to enter into the intricacies and conditions which determine the pressure gradients over the primary and secondary sealing areas. It suffices to recognise the existence of these pressure gradients and to remember that the effectiveness of piston rings depends upon the presence of lubricating oil*

Whilst the construction and principles of the Wankel sealing grid have been explained, it may be opportune to refer to other factors which ensure the proper functioning of this grid. Fig. 7.6 shows a cross-section through a sealing element, attention is drawn to its primary and secondary sealing areas as well as to the pressure gradients across these areas. Under a microscope, seemingly flat and smooth surfaces may resemble the wildest part of the Grand Canyon, so that little more than the peaks of mating surfaces will contact each other as the sealing grid moves over the housing surfaces. It is the purpose of the lubricating oil to fill the crevices and, in fact, prevent as far as possible the contact of these peaks. Due to the motion of the grid, and depending on the presence of sufficient oil, there may even be a tendency towards a hydrodynamic wedge. Whether this conjecture is correct or not is of less importance than the realisation that by the very nature of things the pressure at either end of the primary and secondary sealing areas is determined by the respective gas pressure on either side of the seal, and the variation in between may be affected by surface condition. The important thing to note is that there must be a pressure difference across the primary and secondary sealing area if the grid is to function satisfactorily. Since the width of the respective sealing areas is rather small and may vary from 0·03 in–0·1 in even for relatively large displacement engines, it is difficult to devise suitable instrumentation for the verification of the above reasoning and deductions. However, the matter is under consideration and it may become necessary to revise the opinion thus expressed in the light of new evidence which may be forthcoming.

It should not be assumed that a sealing grid can only be executed as shown in Fig. 7.5, other configurations complying with the fundamental principles as set out are possible, Fig. 4.3. Indeed patent office files reveal that not only the licensors and licensees of the NSU/Wankel RC engine have been busily improving known designs and devising new ones.

It is now possible to summarise the essential characteristics of a Wankel sealing grid as follows:

1. Maintenance of indispensable running clearances under all operating conditions and at all temperatures make a gas sealing system essential.
2. The sealing grid of every chamber consists of a system of sealing elements and link blocks which are so joined together as *to ensure continuous primary and secondary sealing area contact.*
3. A sealing grid must be designed capable of accommodating production tolerances, be unaffected by differential thermal expansion without drastic sacrifice of sealing efficiency.
4. The sealing function depends entirely upon the presence of an adequate amount of oil and upon gas pressure, except under starting conditions when light spring pressure is relied upon.
5. A sealing grid must maintain primary and secondary area contact despite possible opposing dynamic or gas forces.
6. It is evident that the above conditions can only be satisfied if the respective sealing grid is accommodated either in a moving or a stationary part, not in both.
7. It is impossible to effect a satisfactory sealing between more than two major components. Sealing is possible either between a stationary housing assembly and one rotor, as in Wankel PLM engines, or between two moving assemblies, as in the original NSU/Wankel SIM type engine, but not between a stationary housing and two moving components, as at least one primary sealing area contact would have to jump from the housing to one of the moving parts to another and back again to the stationary housing as in a gear type pump.

## 7.3. The Side Seals

Although the side seals were developed in line with other components of the Wankel RC engine, they presented no problems which approached those experienced with the apex seals. There was never even a suggestion that they might cause chatter marks, and their durability was never in doubt. Once sealing element and side cover surface materials were satisfactorily matched and adequate lubrication assured the residual problems were not functional but of concern to production engineers.

It is obvious that for satisfactory performance the side cover must present acceptably flat surfaces which remained flat and normal to the output shaft axis under all operating conditions. Those familiar with reciprocating piston water pump carbon type seals will appreciate the problem though it is minimised by at least two important factors. These factors are:

1. Light spring pressure is only relied upon to ensure satisfactory contact under starting conditions, after which gas pressure assumes control.
2. Reasonably flexible side sealing strips are, therefore, advantageous. Furthermore. the relatively low rotor speed — $\frac{1}{3}$rd output shaft speed — makes a useful contribution to satisfactory side seal functioning and their durability.

## 7.4. The Apex Seals

Lack of appreciation of the complexities affecting apex seal behaviour seems to have created the impression that the Wankel RC engine suffers from inherent 'Sealing Problems'. It is, therefore, proposed to look a little closer into the technicalities of apex seal design and performance in the hope that this may lead to a more realistic assessment of what these sealing elements are expected to do and what they really achieve.

As explained in Chapter 3, the bores of Wankel RC engines are chosen larger than true epitrochoids to prevent unnecessary seal movement, to improve heat dissipation and lubrication, and thus promote superior wear characteristics. The apparent widespread belief that line contact between the apex seals and the bores is contributory to bad sealing is surprising. In actual fact the opposite is nearer the truth. To begin with, true line contact is a practical impossibility because of the resilience of the respective materials. Line contact implies contact along a line which has *no* width so that even the smallest force would cause infinite stresses in both components with predictable results. The absence of failure peculiar to this cause suggests that area contact is taking place and other influences, such as hydrodynamic effects, assert themselves beneficially. Indeed, considering the wide range of operating conditions with which the Wankel sealing grid and the apex seals in particular seem to be capable of coping, there would appear to be a ready subject for worthwhile basic research from which other branches of engineering might benefit.

It should perhaps be pointed out that conditions very similar to those between the apex seals and the bore exist in some automotive diesel engines which incorporate a barrelled profile top compression ring to promote 'bedding' in, to use a well-worn phrase. Various oxide finishes are used as well as copper and chrome plating.

At present it may be concluded that the very narrow sealing band and consequently the high contact pressure tend to minimise surface deficiencies invisible to the naked eye. Even the smoothest of surfaces look like a newly ploughed field under an electron microscope, so that so-called 'area contact' is not a reality. Some of the design considerations and operating conditions under which apex seals are expected to function have already been considered, so it is therefore opportune to look at some of the variables which add to the sum total of factors which must be considered when designing a sealing grid, and especially apex seals, for RC engines.

Unfortunately, it is impossible to guarantee a perfect oil film at all times and under all operating conditions, consequently it is important to match bore surface and apex seal materials and their respective hardness so as to ensure satisfactory sealing and minimum wear rates. Various metal spray and electro-chemical methods of depositing metal on the epitrochoidal bore and the side covers have been tried and four combinations of surface and apex seal materials have proved satisfactory by minimising and even completely avoiding the formation of chatter marks round the bore without sacrifice of durability. These combinations are as shown in table 7.1.

**Table 7.1**

| Bore Surface | Apex Seals | Side Covers | Side Seal |
|---|---|---|---|
| Hard Chrome | Carbon | Molybdenum | Piston Ring Cast Iron |
| Cemented Carbide | Cast Iron | Bronze | Cast Iron and Steel |
| 10% Molybdenum + 90% Steel | Soft Iron | Cast Iron Nitrided or Induction Hardened | Piston Ring Cast Iron (Soft) |
| *Nickel plating and simultaneous depositing of Silicon-Carbide particles | Piston Ring Cast Iron | Steel—spray deposited | Piston Ring Cast Iron |

*This process was originally developed in the U.S.A. where it is known as the C.E.M. (Composite Electro-chemical Material) depositing process.

Undoubtedly other combinations will emerge during the course of time as the investigations continue since some of the depositing operations and finishing processes are perhaps laborious and, therefore, comparatively costly.

As to other variables affecting apex seal performance, the most obvious is the variable speed at which the apex seals slide over the epitrochoidal surface.

Apex seal velocities (see Fig. 7.7) for any shaft angle may be found by using the formula

$$v_a = \frac{\omega_1}{3} \sqrt{\left( 9e^2 + R_1^2 + 6eR_1 \cos \frac{2\alpha}{3} \right)} \tag{7.1}$$

$$\text{Max } v_a = \frac{2\pi n_E \left( \dfrac{R_1}{3} + e \right)}{1{,}000} \quad \text{m/sec } (R_1 \text{ and } e \text{ in mm})$$

$$= \frac{2\pi n_E \left( \dfrac{R_1}{3} + e \right)}{12} \quad \text{ft/sec } (R_1 \text{ and } e \text{ in inches})$$

$$\text{Min } v_a = \frac{2\pi n_E \left( \dfrac{R_1}{3} - e \right)}{12} \quad \text{ft/sec}$$

$$= \frac{2\pi n_E \left( \dfrac{R_1}{3} - e \right)}{1{,}000} \quad \text{m/sec}$$

where ($\alpha = \omega_1 . t$) and ($n_E$ = eccentric shaft rev/sec).

A polar diagram showing the variations in apex velocity is shown in Fig. 7.7, which invites comparison with Fig. 7.4 in which the piston speed and cylinder bore wear pattern of a reciprocating piston engine are shown.

*Amongst other things it may be safely concluded that the conditions causing maximum bore wear in the reciprocating piston engine do not exist in the Wankel RC configuration.*

Figs. 7.8a and b indicate some of the forces which act on apex seals. By far the most important and largest of these is due to gas pressure, though this pressure as well as the resultant force varies as the seal moves round. Considering that the seal moves in a clockwise direction from the minor axis of the epitrochoid, Fig. 7.8, in which $P_1 > P_2$, during the first quarter of a revolution (and the third) the contact line moves from the radial line which passes from the rotor centre of gravity and the apex through the $(-\phi)$ angle.

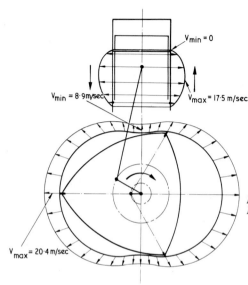

Fig. 7.7. *Cyclic fluctuations of apex velocity of a Wankel RC engine. The basic data of this engine are:*

$$R = 84 \ mm \qquad e = 11 \ mm$$

$$therefore \ \frac{R}{e} = \frac{84}{11} = 7\cdot64 \ and \ \phi = 23°$$

Hence the contact force due to gas pressure will be $P_1 B_c \{2a-(a+a \sin \phi_n)\} - P_2 B_c(a-a \sin \phi_n)$ (7.2) where $\phi_n$ is the actual angle of obliquity at the respective position of the apex seal and $B_c$ is the length of the apex seal, i.e. the axial chamber width.

In the third (and fourth) quarter the contact line moves through the $(+\phi)$ angle round the apex seal nose and the above formula must read

$$P_2 B_c \{2a-(a+a \sin \phi_n)\} - P_1 B_c(a-a \sin \phi_n) \tag{7.3}$$

Calculating the gas forces which tend to keep the apex seals in contact with the bore for various seal positions, and taking into account the pressure variations, it is possible to construct another polar diagram. Add to this the centrifugal force, which also varies due to the sealing element (and spring) c.g. moving in a trochoidal path, and the spring pressure, a fairly accurate picture is obtained for one set of operating conditions. Considering the very light weight of the spring it may be assumed that its mass is part of the apex seal and the shape of the apex seal will facilitate finding the position of its centre of gravity—at a radius $r$ from the rotor centre of gravity.

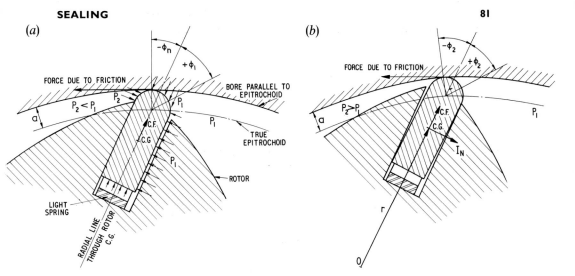

Fig. 7.8. *In Fig. 7.8a gas pressure* $P_1$ *is greater than* $P_2$, *whereas Fig. 7.8b is meant to illustrate the point when* $P_2$ *has become greater than* $P_1$ *and is, therefore, pushing the apex seal forward in the direction of rotation i.e. against friction drag*

The fundamental formula for centrifugal force

$$\text{c.f.} = \frac{Wv^2}{gr} = M\omega^2 r$$

is slightly modified to accommodate the variations of the effective radius of the centre of gravity and reads

$$\text{c.f.} = \left(\frac{r}{9} + e \cos 2\alpha\right) \omega_1^2 \cdot \frac{W}{g} \tag{7.4}$$

and

$$(\text{c.f.})_{\text{max}} = \left(\frac{r}{9} + e\right) \omega_1^2 \cdot \frac{W}{g} \text{ whilst } (\text{c.f.})_{\text{min}} = \left(\frac{r}{9} - e\right) \omega_1^2 \cdot \frac{W}{g}$$

Attention must be drawn to somewhat indeterminate conditions which occur when $P_2$ becomes greater than $P_1$ besides being capable of overcoming the friction component Fig. 7.8b. Under these conditions the apex seal may tend to tilt towards contact on its leading secondary sealing area. The amount of tilt is limited by the essential clearance between the apex seal and the slot accommodating it. Due to apex velocity variations already described there will be inertia forces $I_N$ normal to the apex seals which may tend to assist or resist this occurrence. Certainly under these circumstances the apex seal will be momentarily deprived of adequate contact with a secondary sealing area, surface conditions at the contact line with the bore may excite the apex seal into vibration and possibly promote the formation of chatter marks. Clearly this is a complex problem and the above sequence of events is largely conjecture as experimental verification has so far proved rather elusive.

The inertia force normal to the apex seal $I_N$ is found as follows:

$$I_N = e\omega_1^2 \frac{W}{g} \sin 2\alpha \qquad\qquad\qquad (7.5)$$

$$\therefore \quad I_{N\max} = +e \cdot \omega_1^2 \cdot \frac{W}{g} \qquad I_{N\min} = -e \cdot \omega_1^2 \cdot \frac{W}{g}$$

Whilst it is relatively easy to determine the temperature variations round the epitro-choidal bore, Fig. 7.9, it is far more difficult to ensure and check whether the apex seals

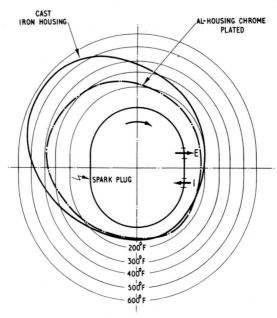

Fig. 7.9. Temperature variations round the bore of a Wankel RC engine when no attempts have been made to reduce the temperature differences. The distribution in a cast iron and a light alloy housing is compared. The volumetric displacement was 250 cm³ per shaft revolution. The temperature was measured 1 mm below the surface of the bore

are satisfactorily lubricated over the combustion and expansion phases under all operating conditions. So far evidence suggests that an adequate amount of lubrication is being maintained on the epitrochoidal surface over a surprisingly wide engine performance range. Dry lubrication and sealing systems requiring no lubrication at all are distinct possibilities and may form the core of some intensive research.

Meanwhile it may be opportune to reiterate that the Wankel sealing grid has proved satisfactory and durable. The essential features of such a sealing grid are:

1. Continuous primary sealing area contact.
2. Continuous secondary sealing area contact.
3. Presence of oil.
4. The grid must be designed to accommodate normal production tolerances.
5. The grid must be designed to accommodate differential thermal expansion.

6. The grid relies primarily upon gas pressure to effect sealing, except under starting conditions.

7. There must be a lower pressure outside the grid if sealing is to be effected.

Before concluding this very important chapter on the gas sealing systems of Wankel RC engines it should be pointed out that whilst one-piece apex seals have given a satisfactory account of themselves, it is now preferred to use a three-piece design in which the triangular corner pieces compensate, up to a point, for any end wear which may occur. It should also be recognised that the pattern of pressure changes in all three chambers minimises or restricts to some extent leakages from one chamber into those adjacent. There is no doubt that detailed study of the sealing and wear problems made a major contribution to the notable results already achieved by Wankel type RC engines.

# 8

# The Porting—Side and Peripheral Inlet Ports and their Merits, Gas Velocity and Volumetric Efficiency

Internal combustion engine performance depends entirely upon the requisite amount of air and fuel getting into the cylinders or working chambers. Admission of this mixture, charge or gas, as it is commonly called, is made possible by the reduction in pressure which is being created by piston movement. The magnitude of this reduction depends on the rate of volume variation, the effective valve or port opening area, the restriction due to induction port shape, length and cross-sectional area plus the restriction caused by the carburettor, the choke, the throttle and air cleaner or intake silencer, not forgetting exhaust back pressure variations due to exhaust efflux and temperature effects.

The valve opening and closing process controls the gas flow in reciprocating piston engines up to about the point at which the effective valve opening area, permitting the passage of gas, equals the cross-sectional area uncovered by the throttle. Beyond that instant, the controlling function is assumed by the throttle, but reverts again to the valve at the appropriate moment during the closing phase. It is perhaps difficult to envisage the continuous passing of the control function from the throttle to the valve and back again. However, it is important to realise that the controlling function is always assumed by the smallest effective area through which the gas must flow irrespective of whether this occurs at the valve, throttle or choke. In practice these cyclic variations of the control function between valve and throttle are normally unnoticeable, but attention is drawn to this phenomena because it is of lesser significance in the case of RC engines, a deduction based on the differences of the port opening diagrams Fig. 2.7b–e. It is noticeable that a poppet valve is only momentarily completely open whereas the opening and closing phases of the Wankel RC engine extend over a very short period in comparison with the time during which the ports are completely open. Much more rapid opening is possible, if need be, by suitably shaping the ports.

*The pattern of gas velocity variations within the induction system of the Wankel RC engine is, therefore not the same as in reciprocating piston engines.*

Apart from the differences already pointed out, the peripheral ports of the Wankel RC engine are never closed, an apex seal passing over a port merely cuts the chamber ahead of it from the port and simultaneously opens the respective port to the chamber on its trailing side.

The quantity of gas flowing into the chambers may be said to be a function of the port area and the duration of its opening. A given volume of gas may be passed either through a small port open for a comparatively long time, or through a larger port open for a shorter period. For understandable reasons the larger ports are generally preferred for two-stroke engines, but much greater latitude prevails in Wankel RC engines because the exhaust and inlet phases may be spaced more sensibly within the broad range of those of conventional four-stroke engines.

Although both the exhaust and inlet ports are intended to pass the same amount of gas, each makes its own peculiar demands. For instance, the exhaust ports are intended to ensure rapid evacuation of the spent gases which may be promoted by quick opening periods and minimum restriction within the exhaust system as a whole. The precise timing of the beginning and end of every exhaust phase is obviously a design function, excessively early opening, when gas pressure is still high, making for a noisier engine than later opening. However, overlap of induction and exhaust periods will be chosen relative to the expected speed range of the engine and, as far as the geometry of the respective RC engine permits (see Fig. 2.7b–e) peripheral ports tending towards large nominal overlap periods and side inlet ports reduce this considerably at the expense of late opening, that is at the t.d.c. position or even afterwards.

Considerable cumulative information is available about the flow of liquids or gases through orifices, accordingly widely differing flow rates may be obtained with nominally identical areas, the results depending upon the manner in which the respective bore merges with the container. For instance, the flow rate through an exhaust port which has sharp edges where it merges into the epitrochoidal bore may permit a flow rate of barely 75% compared with an equal size port which is suitably rounded where it merges with the bore; superior flow rates are attainable if the exhaust may also be made convergent/divergent in the manner of a Venturi. It is no simple task to apply these flow theories to internal combustion engines—two stroke or RC designs—as other factors must also be taken into account and may even acquire overriding importance under some operating conditions.

Indeed, sharp edged ports opening very rapidly at the right moment may be preferable because the sudden efflux of gas may create a pressure drop within the chamber which may subsequently assist induction. Most Wankel RC engines examined to date simply relied upon sharp edges where the ports joined the bore, only a few having small radii. In general the situation is similar to that prevailing in the two-stroke engine field where such refinements are incorporated only if they are strictly compatible with the application for which the engine is being produced. Considerations of this order would seem to gain significance only at very much higher speed and performance levels than those of current

Wankel RC engines, and even under these conditions it remains to be seen whether any beneficial effects are confined to too narrow a speed band towards the top end.

Be that as it may, gases, mixture or air — if fuel injection is used — must be able to enter and leave the working chambers of any internal combustion engine, but in view of their extraordinarily wide speed range and performance characteristics it would be wrong to assume that the gas replenishment process is always equally efficient. The ratio of $V_a/V_s$ is termed volumetric efficiency, and for a normally aspirated engine

$$\frac{V_a}{V_s} = \frac{\text{Volume induced per charge at ambient conditions} \times 100}{\text{Theoretical displacement volume at ambient conditions}} \%$$

However, pressure and temperature effects ought to be taken into account, so that it is preferred to work out the ratio of the masses

$$\eta_{mass} = \frac{\text{Actual mass of charge admitted per induction phase} \times 100}{\substack{\text{Maximum theoretical mass which could be admitted under} \\ \text{ambient conditions}}} \%$$

If $P_a$ and $T_a$ represent ambient pressure and temperature
   $V_s$ = swept or displacement volume (calculated)
   $m$ = mass actually admitted per induction phase (measured)
   $R$ = gas constant

$$\text{Maximum theoretical mass of charge} = m_a = \frac{P_a \times V_s}{T_a \times R}$$

$$\text{and} \qquad\qquad m = \frac{P \times V_a}{T \times R}$$

where $P$ and $T$ are the pressure and temperature of the charge within the respective chamber.

$$V_a = \frac{\text{Volume admitted per min}}{\text{Shaft rev/min}}$$

Therefore, mass ratio or gravimetric efficiency $= \eta_{mass} = \dfrac{m \times 100}{m_a} \%$ \hfill (8.1)

Evidently Equation 8.1 applies to any positive displacement engine irrespective of whether it is a reciprocating piston or RC engine. Furthermore, it would be wrong to assume a precise mathematical relationship between port cross-sectional area and volumetric efficiency, though high volumetric efficiency can only be attained if there is little restriction, that is if there is a low pressure drop in the induction system. A low pressure drop in the induction system is a prerequisite of high engine speed though the issue is not quite so simple. Effective port area and the timing of the start and finish of port opening and closing periods — the equivalent of valve timing of reciprocating piston engines —

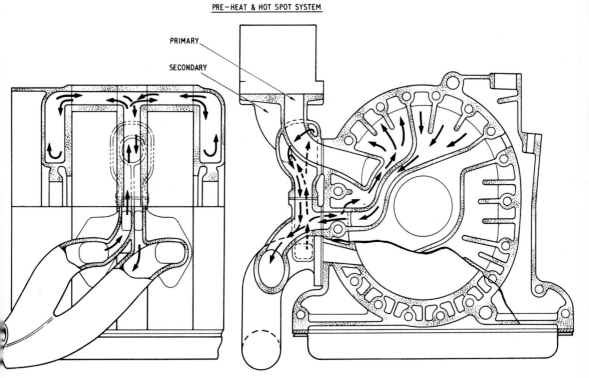

### TYPE OF INDUCTION SYSTEM
#### ENGINE 500 cm³ × 2

**3 BARREL CARBURETTOR & COMBI PORT**

(a)

**3 BARREL CARBURETTOR & SIDE PORT**

(b)

**2 BARREL CARBURETTOR & SIDE PORT**

(c)

| PORT TIMING | | 3 BARREL CARB. & COMBI PORT | 2, 3 BARREL CARB. & SIDE PORT |
|---|---|---|---|
| INLET OPENS | p | 39° A.T.D.C. | 39° A.T.D.C. |
| | s | 103° B.T.D.C. | 39° A.T.D.C. |
| INLET CLOSES | p | 33° A.B.D.C | 33° A.B.D.C. |
| | s | 42° A.B.D.C | 52° A.B.D.C. |
| EXHAUST OPENS | | 68° B.B.D.C | 68° B.B.D.C. |
| EXHAUST CLOSES | | 57° A.T.D.C. | 57° A.T.D.C. |

*Fig. 8.1. Diagrammatic arrangement of induction systems of various editions of the Toyo Kogyo twin rotor engine*

### PRE−HEAT & HOT SPOT SYSTEM

PRIMARY

SECONDARY

*Fig. 8.2. Pre-heat and hot spot system as applied to Toyo Kogyo twin rotor engines*

has a bearing on the maximum possible speed of any positive displacement engine. Volumetric efficiency varies also with respect to the heat acquired by the charge on its way from the carburettor to the working chamber since under the operating conditions gas density decreases as the temperature rises. However, other considerations would seem to favour a more equitable temperature distribution round the entire housing, which could be brought about by

1. cooling the hot side of the engine to a lower temperature
2. heating the cold side of the engine by passing exhaust gases round it
3. relying upon both 1. and 2.

Toyo Kogyo in Japan seems to have achieved (3) without sacrificing engine efficiency, Figs. 8.1 and 8.2 showing the diagrammatic port arrangement of the Toyo Kogyo twin rotor engine as well as the pre-heat and hot spot system which are responsible for the temperature distribution round the bore illustrated in Fig. 8.3. The effect of pre-heat arrangement is that at 3,000 rev/min, the centre housing temperature is raised by 51·2°C in position A, whilst the temperature at the hottest portion, position E, is lowered by 12·2°C. Similarly at 6,000 rev/min, the rise in temperature at A is 63°C and the reduction of temperature at $E$ is 10°C. Equally important is the pattern of temperature distribution round the bore which tends to be symmetrical, and which minimises any problems that might arise due to differential thermal expansion and difficult to control distortions resulting from it. It is interesting to note that at 5,000 rev/min, the temperature rise at position $A$ exceeds that at 6,000 rev/min, which suggests that the optimum capability of the pre-heat arrangement was well chosen for the particular engine.

This Toyo Kogyo engine incorporates other novel features apart from the temperature equalisation system, for instance this engine may be fitted with a three barrel carburettor feeding into the chambers by way of a single siamese side (primary) inlet port at idling and over the lower load and speed range, whereas at the upper load and speed range suitably controlled throttle valves open a single peripheral (secondary) port into each chamber unit for improved performance. This is the arrangement of the high performance engine, which develops 118 b.h.p. yet idles smoothly down to very low shaft speeds.

Fig. 2.7a–e were deliberately shown in close proximity to each other with the individual thermodynamic phases stretched over the same distance in order to permit a realistic comparison of valve and port timing. After all the important factor is not shaft rotation, but valve and/or port timing relative to the volume variations within the respective engines. Expressing the overlap periods as percentages of a single phase − 180° = 100% for reciprocating piston engines and 270° also = 100% for the RC engines − it will be noted that the overlap range of the 20 reciprocating piston engines examined spans 55%, whereas the overlap of the NSU/Wankel KKM 502 engine amounts to 74% at the higher loads when the peripheral inlet port is in use, but it is confined to 45·4% under the important idling conditions and for loads up to 30% of full load.

The Toyo Kogyo engine on the other hand has 6·7% overlap when the primary ports (side inlet) are in use, and 59·3% in the upper performance range when the secondary (peripheral) inlet ports are operative.

Whilst the port opening and closing curves shown in Fig. 2.7a–e are those applicable

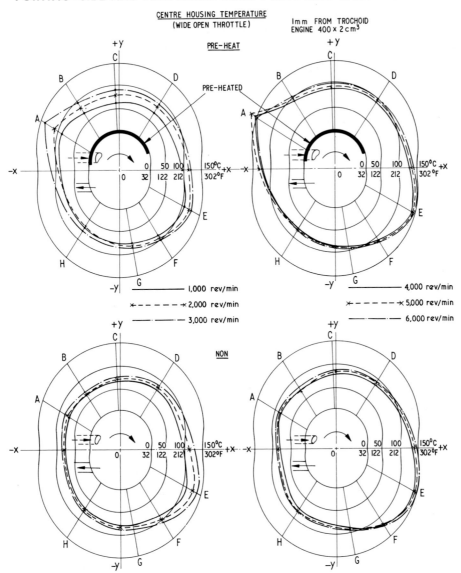

Fig. 8.3. Comparison of temperature distribution round the bores of Toyo Kogyo twin rotor RC engines at various shaft speeds when pre-heat is applied (top) and when no pre-heat system has been provided. The more equitable temperature distribution with pre-heat minimises problems associated with differential thermal expansion of engine casings

to the respective engines, the overlap periods of the Wankel RC engines have by no means the same significance as the valve opening overlap of reciprocating piston engines. This apparent anomaly is due to the fact that nominal port opening and closing is determined by the apex seals passing over the peripheral ports—or the rotor uncovering the side inlet ports—whilst effective overlap is controlled by the beginning and end of the depression in every rotor flank as they pass the nominal sealing line between the rotor flank and the epitrochoidal bore in the vicinity of the minor axis. This must be considered a potential sealing line or severe restriction, because no actual contact occurs between the rotor flanks and the epitrochoidal bore, as they are separated merely by the requisite minimum running clearance.

The same nominal sealing occurs, of course, on the hot side of the engine which, for practical purposes, divides the chamber into two variable volume parts, which communicate with each other by way of the depression in the respective rotor flank. Indeed, the bottom and sides of the depression and part of the epitrochoidal bore define a transfer passage – most likely to be of variable cross-section – through which the mixture must pass from the trailing to the leading part of the chamber. It stands to reason that this transfer velocity, and any turbulence it may cause, has important effects on combustion, which could be greater than that of 'squish' in reciprocating piston engines, because the whole mixture must pass through this variable cross-section transfer passage.

Although the characteristics of only four Wankel RC engine port arrangements are illustrated by the curves of Fig 2.7b–e it is possible to conclude that design geometry controls the beginning and end of the port opening periods. Peripheral ports cannot be opened much later or closed much earlier than indicated without jeopardising effectively attainable compression ratios, the controlling factor being the distance between adjacent apex seals. Despite this limitation there is considerable latitude in selecting sudden or gradual opening and closing curves as may be deemed essential for the respective engine application.

Side port opening and closing curves, on the other hand, are essentially sinusoidal, and unfortunately the beginning of the inlet port opening period cannot be easily advanced up to or before the t.d.c. position without sacrifice in other directions. Effective overlap can certainly be reduced, but the timing would seem to favour low speed torque and performance. The combination of side and peripheral ports used in conjunction with three and lately four barrel carburettors in the Toyo Kogyo RC engines clearly aims at the root of the apparently contradictory requirements of a sensible high torque and economic fuel consumption in the lower speed range with maximum specific power output at the upper speeds. Indeed, the examples shown, including the NSU/KKM 502 arrangement of primary and secondary inlet ports, by no means exhaust the possible alternatives which may be devised and which may be expected as research into the performance phenomena of RC engines continues.

Valve timing of the familiar reciprocating piston engine relative to the crankshaft t.d.c. position may be chosen, by comparison, within extraordinarily wide limits, commensurate with the desired performance level of the engine. Unfortunately this wide choice does not extend to valve actuation since inertia of the respective valve gear and the capability of the return springs to control the closing phases at all speeds, without excessive valve seating velocities, impose severe limitations, not forgetting the problem of accommodating suitable valve springs within the confined space available.

Desmodromic valve actuation seems capable of postponing the onset of desirable effects due to high speed, but introduces complexities without offering completely to overcome the problem.

Comparison of the valve and port opening diagrams Fig. 2.7a–e suggests that the Wankel RC engine with peripheral ports is basically biased towards the higher speed and performance ranges where attainment depends not upon thermodynamic factors, but on friction, wear phenomena, lubrication and perhaps even ignition.

Although the application for which a particular reciprocating piston engine is to be designed and developed dictates certain performance levels, it is the mean mixture velocity through the effective valve openings for maximum power conditions which also has far reaching effects on the torque characteristics at the lower speed range. For instance, the high mean inlet gas velocity of some Coventry Climax Formula One racing engines handsomely exceeds 400 ft/sec, at the crankshaft speed at which maximum power is developed. Consequently there seems to be adequate turbulence within the combustion chamber down to the lower speed range, to promote good combustion and, therefore, good torque characteristics. Inlet gas velocities of more ordinary production type engines are much lower even at maximum engine speed of 5,000 rev/min, or so. Designers seem to pursue different philosophies when proportioning inlet valve openings for maximum inlet gas velocity and maximum power, but broadly speaking, it appears that high gas velocities for maximum power promote good volumetric efficiency, adequate turbulence and sensible b.m.e.p. levels in the lower crankshaft speed range.

The mean gas velocity for maximum power of reciprocating piston engines is the product of mean piston speed multiplied by the ratio of bore cross-sectional area, over effective valve opening area. That is

$$\text{Mean gas velocity} = c = \frac{2Sn}{12} \times \frac{A}{a}$$

$$= \frac{Sn}{6} \times \frac{A}{a} \text{ ft/min}$$

where
$S$ = stroke in inches
$n$ = rev/min.
$A$ = bore cross-sectional area in sq. in.
$a$ = effective valve opening area in sq. in.

For the Wankel RC engine it was found expedient to re-arrange and modify this formula to suit.

$$\text{Mean gas velocity } c = \frac{\text{Displacement (in}^3) \times \text{Shaft speed (rev/min)}}{\text{Port cross-sectional area (in}^2) \times 12 \times 60 \times \frac{3}{4}} \text{ (ft/sec)} \qquad (8.2)$$

$$= \frac{\text{Displacement (cm}^3) \times \text{Shaft speed (rev/min)}}{1000 \times \text{port cross-sectional area (cm}^2) \times 4\cdot5} = \text{m/sec}$$

The factors $\frac{3}{4}$ and $\dfrac{1}{4\cdot5}$ are due to the fact that the induction period, like any other, extends

over 270° or $\frac{3}{4}$ of a revolution $\qquad \dfrac{1}{4\cdot5} = \dfrac{360°}{6 \times 270°}$ .

In the case of the NSU/KKM 502 engine, as fitted to the NSU Spider car, the mean gas velocity at $6,000$ rev/min $= \dfrac{30 \cdot 012 \times 6,000 \times 4}{1 \cdot 508 \times 12 \times 60 \times 3} = 221 \cdot 1$ ft/sec or $67 \cdot 44$ m/sec. However, an additional factor must be taken into account in Wankel RC engines since over part of the port opening period the effective opening area is determined by the proximity of the rotor flank to the port and the combustion chamber is, in fact divided on the hot side of the engine and between the ports by the necking in of the epitrochoidal bore within the proximity of the minor axis. The variable volume chamber sections are interconnected by the depression in the rotor flanks. Unless these depressions are of large cross-sectional area relative to the compressed mixture volume, it is evident that the transfer velocity $(V_t)$ through the depression can promote additional swirl at a crucial moment during combustion. Modern compression ratio requirements effect the choice of the actual depression volume; moreover it is already known that effective cross-sectional area,

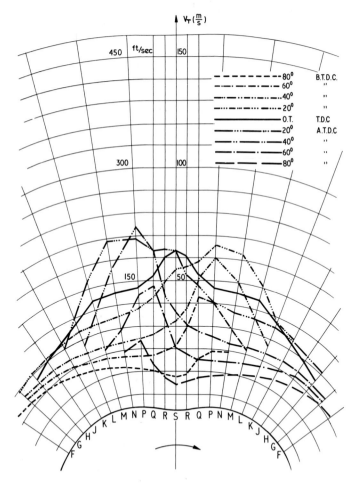

Fig. 8.4. Transfer velocity pattern of the KKM 502 engine at 6,000 rev/min, and with a symmetrical depression in every rotor flank

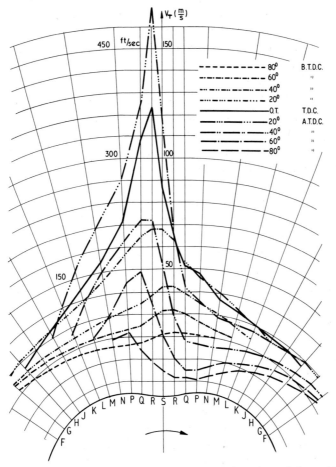

*Fig. 8.5. Transfer velocity pattern of the KKM 502 engine at 6,000 rev/min., but with forward located depression in every rotor flank. Selecting the relative position of the depressions in the rotor flanks speeds flame propagation and permits tailoring of performance characteristics to application requirements*

position and shape of the depression affects turbulence and has, therefore, a beneficial effect on combustion in general.

Most research and development work so far was carried out with symmetrical depressions in the rotor flanks, with some notable exceptions. Dr. Ing. W. Froede pointed out, in his James Clayton lecture on 8 February 1966 that these transfer or tangential velocities may reach about 200 ft/sec, when depressions are symmetrical, but close on 500 ft/sec, can be attained by locating the depressions in the leading portion of each rotor flank. Figs. 8.4 and 8.5 illustrate this occurrence, the significance of which is only just beginning to be recognised.

There is no doubt that the evaluation of these gas velocities is a complex task, moreover it is perhaps even more difficult, at this stage, to use the results for much more than comparative purposes, for their validity as design criteria has yet to be proved.

High speed photographic records of the combustion phase within the Wankel RC engine—made at Curtiss-Wright in the U.S.A. and Toyo Kogyo in Japan—showed that flame propagation is made up of two parts, namely by adding the flame advance rate relative to the mass of the charge, to the tangential velocity of the orbiting charge. This phenomena was confirmed by suitably disposed ionisation detection plugs connected to the requisite electronic recording devices.

The designer of Wankel RC engines is, therefore, in the fortunate position of being able to influence, or even control combustion phenomena, a liberty which is more limited in the case of ordinary Otto-cycle reciprocating piston engine design. Furthermore, it may safely be surmised that flame propagation within a moving mixture is made up of mixture velocity plus flame movement within the mixture and, since the latter is in absolute terms relatively low, flame propagation is primarily in the direction of mixture travel. Whether any limiting or modifying influences assert themselves eventually is not yet known, though on the basis of available data they are unlikely to become apparent in existing and contemplated high speed Wankel RC engines. It remains to be seen to what extent it is possible to improve combustion under the many varying load and speed conditions encountered by the average car engine. The portents are that the more complete combustion thus achieved could significantly improve exhaust emission of the Wankel RC engine.

It is perhaps pertinent in this connection to suggest that multi-ignition may effect further improvements in combustion as indicated by Figs. 23 to 26 of Dr. Ing. W. Froede's James Clayton lecture (Figs. 6.17, 6.18, 11.1 and 11.2); they show that encouraging results have been achieved already in limited work on dual ignition engines.

Whilst most remarks about combustion phenomena of Wankel RC engines apply to RC engines irrespective of their induction port arrangements, it seems advisable to differentiate between engines having peripheral inlet ports and those with side inlet ports. Peripheral inlet ports appear to favour high speed performance, whilst side inlet ports give improved bottom end performance at the sacrifice of volumetric efficiency, and consequently power output in the upper speed range. Speculation as to the degree of sophistication required, which would eventually lead to engines with peripheral ports having adequate low and high speed performance characteristics is obviously premature, though efforts are continuing to improve performance characteristics of engines having either, or even both, induction port arrangements. Fig. 8.1a which shows a dual port high performance engine under development at Toyo Kogyo Co. Ltd. of Japan illustrates the enormous scope confronting design and development engineers. The most important point is that the purpose of RC engine research is not to prove or disprove pet theories, but to obtain the best possible overall engine performance and, if need be, to point to the merits and/or disadvantages of certain design features and their suitability for specific engine applications, and/or the need for further investigation and research.

It should perhaps be pointed out that certain Toyo Kogyo engines with side inlet ports on both sides of the rotor have practically the same top end performance as engines with peripheral inlet ports

# 9

# Lubrication

Whilst it may safely be assumed that modern lubrication techniques and lubricants owe a great deal to the phenomenal success and development of the reciprocating piston engine, it is perhaps surprising that relatively little is known about lubrication as such. This realisation is forced home whenever new devices or mechanisms, such as the Wankel RC engine, create new problems which are glibly referred to as lubrication problems. It must also be admitted that any lubrication problem is an extraordinarily complex issue which may be split into several separate parts, namely:

1. The operating conditions.
2. Lubricant characteristics.
3. Other influences, for example the evaporation and combustion of the lubricant, which is peculiar to internal combustion engines.
4. Physical and chemical changes in the lubricant under service conditions.

These complexities are further emphasised by the fact that operating conditions, especially of engines, are in themselves influenced by a number of varying factors. It can be said that *operating conditions* are influenced by

1. Often varying dynamic factors.
2. Temperature factors, which can also vary.
3. Surface condition, smoothness, hardness etc.
4. Materials of the parts which move relative to each other.

No doubt one could add to this list, or even differentiate between individual factors which combine to form the lubrication characteristics, but this seems to be the prerogative of the lubrication specialists, chemists or physicists who specialise in this work.

It is the poor engineer who is left with the practically impossible task of ensuring that adequate engine durability is provided despite the many, often conflicting, influences which seem to favour high friction and considerable wear rates.

In the case of the Wankel RC engine it is necessary to distinguish between the lubrication requirements of the shaft and rotor housings, as well as of the phasing gear, and the lubrication requirements of the apex seals and the bore. In addition, it may be reiterated that the function of sealing agent is also assigned to the lubricating oil, as explained in Chapter 7.

In liquid cooled Wankel RC engines there is, broadly speaking, no problem of bearing and gear lubrication since a copious supply of oil is passed through the rotor for cooling purposes. The real problem is associated with the apex seals, though oil which reaches the combustion chamber has no chance to pollute the clean oil passing through the rotor, as it is eventually either burned or ejected together with the exhaust gases.

The Wankel RC engine seems, at least in this one aspect, superior to the reciprocating piston engine, though its wear and durability problem is largely confined to the apex seals and the bore. Before elaborating on this issue it may be advisable to dispose of arguments which may be associated with the sealing function of the oil; that is, the dependency of effective sealing upon the presence of an adequate quantity and quality of oil on the primary and secondary sealing areas as elaborated in Chapter 7. Temperature conditions at and around the elements forming the sealing grid must not cause evaporation or burning of the lubricating oil, because this may lead to residual deposits and eventually cause a complete failure of the sealing grid. The phenomenon is akin to that encountered in reciprocating piston engines, and is prevented from escalating to a problem by using the correct oil – usually found by trial and error in the experimental departments of the engine producer and/or the oil companies – and by ensuring adequate cooling.

As the dynamic conditions affecting the apex seals have been adequately elaborated in Chapter 7, it now remains to re-examine the situation relative to lubrication and durability. To begin with, it is obvious that the simple idea of an oil film or dynamic wedge needs modifying. Undoubtedly neither the reciprocating piston engine nor the Wankel RC engine would present a durability problem if a completely uninterrupted oil film or wedge could be ensured under *all* conditions. The fact that wear takes place suggests that, as expected, metal to metal contact does occur. This is unlikely to be continuous over the whole primary sealing area, and is perhaps best explained by imagining two rough surfaces moving relative to each other with the lubricant filling the deep incisions or crevices between the high points. Wear begins when the high peaks which project through the oil film are knocked off, whilst those which cannot be removed proceed to gouge deep ruts and grooves into the components moving over them. It is also possible that particles which are knocked off accumulate and build up here and there, thereby contributing to further wear and even leading to a complete seizure. Most engineers will have observed characteristic cylinder bore and/or shaft wear marks.

Evidently lubrication between the sealing system and the chamber walls presents characteristic boundary lubrication conditions which were described by experts of the British Petroleum Company Ltd., in a book called 'Industrial Lubrication' as follows:

'*Thin-Film or Boundary Lubrication.* The definition of boundary lubrication is one that has taxed many experts. It is perhaps best defined as the lubrication of surfaces by fluid films so thin that the friction coefficient is influenced by the structure of the lubricant and the nature of the surfaces, but is largely independent of viscosity. This definition avoids confusion with both solid and full fluid-film lubrication, though admitting both combined and intermediate effects.

A fluid lubricant introduced between two bearing surfaces may spread to a micro-scopically thin film that reduces the sliding friction between the surfaces. The peaks of the high spots may still touch, but interlocking occurs only to a limited extent and frictional resistance will be relatively low.

A variety of chemical additives can be incorporated in lubricating oils to improve their properties under boundary lubrication conditions. Many of these additives react with the bearing surfaces to produce an extremely thin layer of solid lubricant, which helps to separate the surfaces and prevent seizure. Oils such as these are known as extreme-pressure (EP) lubricants.'

The inner walls of combustion chambers are affected by the burning mixture and can reach fairly high temperatures, see Fig. 7.9, which tends to alter the viscosity of the oil, and, if the temperature continues to rise, may lead to evaporation and eventual combustion of the lubricants. High speed film recordings of the combustion process within Diesel engines, made by Messrs. Ricardo & Co. Engineers (1927) Ltd., and similar photographic records from other sources seem to encourage the belief that the flame never touches the chamber walls, except perhaps in odd spots. This statement must not be interpreted as a gospel truth since Ricardo and Company also indicate that the visible yellow flame within the combustion chamber is preceded by a pale blue flame which has so far defied attempts at photographic recording. Clarification of this issue may in time call for a revision of certain assumptions and conclusions, but meanwhile it suffices to recognise that combustion chamber wall temperatures tend to rise within the limitations of the fuel used, and of the respective cooling arrangement. However, even the permissible temperature increase suffices to alter the viscosity of lubricants, which increases friction besides reducing the damping effects on the apex seal. These are vital factors which tend to permit apex seal chatter and eventually lead to excessive bore and apex seal wear, not forgetting the possibility of the apex seals breaking.

In practice research has shown that appropriate surface finishes, matching of materials and the use of adequate lubricants can overcome these dangers – see p 79. Indeed, dur-ability levels of 1,000–2,000 hr, i.e. a conservative 30,000–80,000 road miles, are being achieved. High viscosity lubricants are known to exert superior damping effects on the apex seals. Apparently these damping effects are reduced as the temperature rises, and they are in any case insufficient in themselves to prevent entirely the formation of chatter marks.

Although it should now be possible to differentiate between the sealing function, which can be satisfied by detail design of the sealing grid, and the complementary dynamic or lubrication problem affecting durability and wear, it is obvious that there is still con-siderable scope for further research. In fact, it is likely that the complexities of these problems will be as persistent as wear and durability problems which have beset the reciprocating piston engine since 1878. There is perhaps hope that with regard to Wankel RC engines, a happy state may be reached where, by and large, wear may be confined to the apex seals, so that merely the replacement of these relatively inexpensive items con-stitutes a periodic servicing requirement. Volumetric efficiencies in excess of 100% indicate that the dual function of the lubricating oil was correctly assessed, moreover results so far achieved are not only satisfactory, but compare favourably with those of the familiar reciprocating piston engine.

At the start of the NSU/Wankel project it was found convenient to lubricate the rotor and sealing elements by mixing one part of oil to every fifty parts of fuel – by volume – as has long been the practice in the two-stroke engine field. Fichtel & Sachs, the first licensee to go into production with Wankel RC engines, still recommend adding 2–2·5% of oil by volume to the fuel – SAE 30 or 40, or approved equivalent. SAE 10W/40 is recommended for the lubrication of the NSU Spider engine, the oil consumption of which amounted to 1·7–2 pints per 1000 miles at the development standard prevailing towards the end of 1965. It is known that considerable progress in lowering these figures has since been made, so that there is no difference in this respect to equal power reciprocating

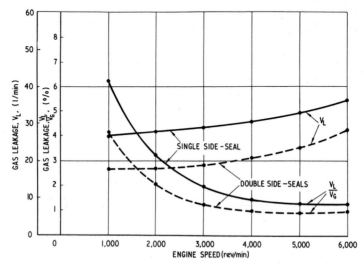

Fig. 9.1. Gas leakages of the NSU KKM 502 RC engine with single and with the latest double side-seals. The specific gas leakage which is $\dfrac{actual\ leakage\ volume}{displacement\ volume}$ expressed in percentage is particularly instructive

piston engines. The problem was very largely one of finding suitable methods of introducing sufficiently minute quantities of oil at the right time and place. Direct injection at several positions round the epitrochoidal bore was certainly beset by metering problems. Various other methods were tried, but metered injection in close proximity to the carburettor is favoured at present, as it brought about a notable reduction in oil consumption. Moreover, the oil is well mixed with the charge, whilst turbulence ensures wetting of the requisite surfaces. Daimler Benz at one time proposed using a metal wick in the induction port, close to where it merged into the epitrochoidal bore, to which they metered oil from a special plunger type pump, whilst others seem to prefer to rely upon controlled leakage past the sealing system. This method of lubrication would seem to ensure lubrication right round the epitrochoidal bore, and an adequate lubrication of the primary and secondary sealing areas of the whole sealing grid. It remains to be seen whether this method is acceptable and simple enough even for small types of engines.

With regard to the side seals, Dr. Ing. W. Froede stated in his James Clayton Lecture, 8 February 1966:

'*The gas leakage over the side-seal is illustrated in Fig. 9.1. This leakage plays an important part in connection with the function of the oil seal and lubrication of the side seals. It consists of unburned mixture and is inflammable. This means that it must occur during compression and probably takes place when the centrifugal forces on the side-seal segments and the gas forces from the initial compression are in balance. At this moment the side-seals change their contact from the outer wall of the annular groove to the inner wall and permit a trace of gas-air mixture to escape. The oil content of this leakage is vital for the lubrication of the contact area between side-seal and side housing.*'

# 10

# Engine Cooling

## 10.1. Introduction

Although most text books on thermodynamics contain sufficient information for the determination of thermal efficiency of various types of heat engines in everyday use, the true state of affairs is seldom appreciated. Thermal efficiency $\eta$, which is defined as the ratio of $\dfrac{\text{Heat supplied} - \text{heat rejected}}{\text{heat supplied}}$ amounts to barely 28% for average gasoline engines and notable improvements of this figure are not easily attainable. An approximate heat balance chart is shown in Table 10.1.

Table 10.1

| | |
|---|---|
| Heat converted into useful work | 28% |
| Heat rejected with exhaust gases | 43% |
| Heat dissipated by coolant | 20% |
| Heat lost to lubricants by radiator etc. | 9% |
| *HEAT SUPPLIED | 100% |

*Note HEAT SUPPLIED

The specific gravity of petrol varies between ·70 and ·77, and the gross calorific value amounts to about 18,700 Btu/lb. If the thermal efficiencies of various engines are to be compared it is suggested that gasoline from the same barrel is used or, if this is impossible , determine the specific gravity and calorific value of the petrol used to permit calculation of the exact amount of heat supplied to the engine on test and thus make an equitable comparison. The reasons for the apparent wide variation of specific gravity are rather complex and have to do with the refining process of the respective gasoline. It should be noted that the calorific value of a fuel is not related to its octane rating, nor does it vary significantly with octane number; consequently nothing is to be gained by using a fuel with a higher octane number than that required by the particular engine.

Very large marine and stationary type Diesel engines may, by comparison, have thermal efficiencies of up to 42%.

Strictly speaking, the expression 'thermal efficiency' describes a rather complex relationship which takes into account the proportion of potential heat converted and the dynamics of combustion, which depends upon the fuel/air ratio, the proportion and constitution of the vaporised fuel, the composition of the fuel itself, ignition effectiveness, mixture turbulence, mixture temperature and chamber wall temperature.

Various factors have determining effects on thermal efficiency, as for instance the compression ratio. The empirical relationship between thermal efficiency and compression ratio is shown in Fig. 10.1. Similarly the higher the permissible engine running temperature, the higher the thermal efficiency—axioms which apply to reciprocating and to RC engines alike. Extreme caution would appear appropriate in the case of Wankel RC engines, as results achieved so far suggest that at best the relationship between compression ratio and thermal efficiency is only approximately within the limits shown for compression ratios of 6 to 1 up to 10 to 1.

The highest permissible compression ratio of an engine is affected by the anti-knock quality of the fuel, usually expressed by the Octane number or rating of the respective gasoline. Detonation or knock can, of course, also be promoted by excessive engine temperature or local hot spots, nevertheless it seems that the highest permissible temperatures of the pistons, the cylinders, the cylinder head and valves etc., is still of overriding

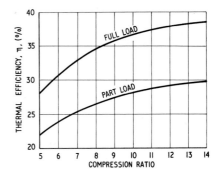

*Fig. 10.1. The greatest care is necessary with regard to the relationship of thermal efficiency and compression ratio because actual values for specific engines depend on many virtually imponderable factors. This figure illustrates therefore, only a general trend*

importance, bearing in mind that combustion temperatures in excess of 2,000°C are high enough to melt aluminium, cast iron and even steel. Fortunately, there is a difference between maximum momentary combustion gas temperature and piston or cylinder wall temperatures; it is one of the tasks of the cooling system to prevent or even out any tendency towards local hot spots. As present day automotive engines run at average coolant temperatures of 70°–90°C, higher temperatures seem desirable because they raise thermal efficiency and can bring about cleaner exhaust emission. However, this must not be achieved at a sacrifice of volumetric efficiency and subsequent power loss, or lead to excessive vaporisation or involuntary ignition. Surface temperatures of components in direct contact with the combustion process or the exhaust gases are, of course, greatly in excess of the above quoted figure. Nevertheless, these parts must retain sufficient strength to withstand the pressures and strains to which they are subjected without significant distortion. Running the engine at too low a temperature not only reduces thermal efficiency, but may prevent satisfactory vaporisation of the fuel with detrimental effects upon ignition and combustion, not to mention undesirable dilution of the lubricating oil. In the Wankel RC engine conditions are not entirely the same; for instance, only the rotor casing and rotor must retain sufficient strength at the running temperature to contain the high pressure and high temperature mixture. There is no possibility of lubricant dilution by unburned petrol since sealing grid lubrication relies entirely upon the total loss lubrication. Moreover. the rotor casing and the rotor of the NSU/KKM 502 and of Toyo Kogyo twin rotor RC engines are made from conventional engineering materials — aluminium and/or cast iron — whilst the apex seals are made from a special type of carbon which is inherently capable of operating satisfactorily at much higher temperatures.

The real problem of ensuring optimum engine temperature over a wide load and speed range is complicated by the fact that car engines run characteristically mostly under part load conditions. For instance, it has been found that according to the U.S.A. driving pattern an automobile engine spends

15%     of its life idling
16%     of its life at constant speed
32%     of its life under overrun conditions — engines pushed by inertia.
37%     of its life accelerating.

The percentage of its life where an engine runs under full load and particularly at maximum power and speed must, therefore, be very small indeed, and depends very largely upon road conditions and driver temperament.

Since conventional gasoline fuel is required by the Wankel RC engine and its specific fuel consumption in lb/b.h.p./hr, is, for practical purposes, the same as that of equivalent power reciprocating piston engines, it follows that gas temperatures will also be very similar to those of conventional piston engines, though in the absence of potential hot spots, of valves, valve springs and valve operating devices, higher engine running temperatures seem feasible in future. Meanwhile it may safely be assumed that the heat dissipation capacity of the Wankel engine's cooling system as a whole will differ very little from that of the reciprocating piston engine. It is the local conditions over the combustion and expansion arc of the rotor housing, as well as in the region of the exhaust port, which are different because of uninterrupted contact with the hot gases. In other words, a far greater thermal demand is made upon the particular portion of the rotor casing — conditions for the rotor are less critical because every rotor flank comes in contact with the cold induction charges — and a far more sophisticated coolant flow pattern is required if the rotor casing temperature is to be kept within permissible limits. Cooling systems ranging from complete liquid cooling to complete air cooling have been developed for a wide variety of engine sizes and applications. According to accumulated experience NSU rate the capabilities of their RC engines relative to the cooling system as in Table 10.2.

**Table 10.2**

| Cooling Medium | | Maximum b.m.e.p. % |
|---|---|---|
| Rotor Housing | Rotor | |
| Water | Oil—Peripheral inlet ports | 100 |
| Water | Oil—Side inlet ports | 85 |
| Air | Oil—Peripheral inlet ports | 90 |
| Water | Mixture Side inlet ports | 75 |
| Air | Mixture Side inlet ports | 60 |

N.B. Mixture = Combustible Mixture.

The few parts of a single rotor Wankel RC engine which require cooling are:

1. The rotor housing containing the epitrochoidal bore.
2. The two end covers or housings.
3. The rotor.
4. The sealing elements, especially the apex seals.

As may be partly deduced from Figs. 7.9 and 8.3, the rotor housing presents the most formidable cooling problem on account of the high local gas velocities (transfer velocities plus turbulence) during the combustion phase, which contribute to the high heat transfer rates, especially in the region of the spark plug and at the exhaust port. The comparatively high exhaust gas temperature at full throttle and high b.m.e.p. figures is at least partly due to the extended combustion, which, under certain circumstances, extends right up to the moment when the exhaust port opens. Admittedly research into means and methods of speeding combustion has barely begun, but the portents are certainly promising. Meanwhile improved and temperature responsive local cooling round the critical sections of the epitrochoidal bore seem to give satisfactory results.

## 10.2. Air Cooling

The problem of the greater thermal demands on sections of the rotor housing was thought to restrict air cooling to the smaller and lower powered RC engines unless above-average power requirements of the cooling system are acceptable. Although NSU and other licensees have devoted considerable effort to the development of various smaller single and twin rotor air cooled engines, Curtiss-Wright have shown that 310 b.h.p. air cooled aircraft type Wankel RC engines with a bare dry weight of 285 lb are entirely practical. To achieve this the Curtiss-Wright 'design study took a different approach and held that the engine could be cooled effectively provided a break with the traditional high volume low pressure system was made in favour of a high pressure low flow system, tailored closely to the heat input variation of this particular engine type. Since the cooling power is directly proportional to flow quantity and pressure drop, the total cooling power could be comparable even if the relative balance shifted.' The analysis of various cooling arrangements yielded fundamental conclusions which seemed practical from the design and manufacturing point of view. The following commended itself to the Curtiss-Wright research team:

1. Closely crowded cooling fins, machined round the periphery of the rotor housing.
2. Air circulation to be accelerated over the hot arc of the engine.
3. Air circulation to be retarded over the cooler part of the rotor housing by widening the effective passages in diffuser fashion in the axial and radial direction.
4. By trimming back the fins, which reduced the effective cooling area and increased the air passage still further. Fig. 10.2.
5. Excess air not required for cooling the rotor housing to be diverted for cooling the area of the exhaust port.

The same reasoning was applied to arranging the flow of coolant air over the end covers, though available evidence suggested that it was not necessary to space the fins as closely, even on the hot part of these covers, as round the rotor housing.

It should be emphasised that the Curtiss-Wright air cooled engine referred to above is being developed as an aircraft engine; it relied upon oil cooling of the rotor. Its b.m.e.p. levels are, therefore, practically identical with those of the automotive engine, though less emphasis may have been placed on high torque at low engine speed and performance over a wide speed range. For the particular design Curtiss-Wright succeeded in keeping the power requirements for cooling well below 10% of the net power developed by the engine.

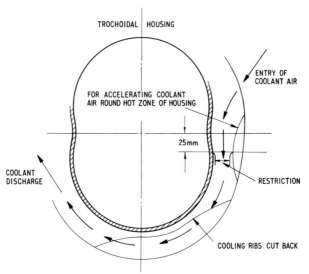

Fig. 10.2. The peripheral flow air cooling system devised by Curtiss-Wright for their research into Wankel RC type aero-engines

The KM 48 Fichtel & Sachs engine is at the other end of the scale, displacing 160 cm$^3$, developing 8·0 b.h.p. at 4700 rev/min, and weighing 37·5 lb. It is, however, a completely air-cooled engine, which means that the induction gases pass alternately through appropriate passages in the eccentric and rotor, and hence through transfer and an axial inlet port, the opening periods of which are controlled by the rotor passing over it. Lubricating oil is added to the fuel as for two stroke engines.

As the induction mixture passes through the rotor, its temperature is raised by about 50°C, which inevitably reduces volumetric efficiency. Consequently the specific power output is restricted and the temperature levels are kept within the capability range of the simple forced draught cooling arrangement as shown in Fig. 10.3 and Plate 10.1.

Air cooled Wankel RC engines for a wide field of applications appear entirely practicable, and do not seem to present any more formidable problems than conventional engines once the peculiarities of their configuration are recognised and understood. Two examples considered, together with the pre-heat arrangement illustrated in Fig. 8.3

suggest that a wide range of sophistication may be incorporated, depending on technical and cost factors acceptable for the respective cooling system and engine design.

NSU as well as Fichtel & Sachs arranged their air coolant flow in a substantially axial direction and obtained adequate dissipating areas by increasing the number of fins per unit length of rotor housing, and by making some fins longer than others, see Fig. 2.1. Obviously these two engines rely, in contrast to the Curtiss-Wright design, upon the high volume/low pressure principle. Attention is also drawn to the location and spacing of

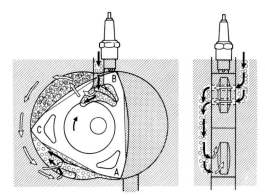

*Fig. 10.3. Mixture flow through rotor for cooling purposes. It should be noted that the primary inlet from the carburettor into the rotor occurs near the spark plug; this arrangement reduces the temperature variation round the epitrochoidal bore*

the clamping bolts within the rather thick metal round the epitrochoidal bore. The NSU/KKM 510 engine is, of course, an industrial type engine for which the small weight penalty is of reduced significance.

## 10.3. Liquid Cooling

To forestall any revival of the controversy over direct air cooled versus liquid cooled engines, let it be understood that modern air cooled engines do not make inordinate demands on power for driving the cooling fans, this being emphasised by the initial success of Curtiss-Wright in developing their RC aircraft engine.

It is known that smooth surfaces absorb less heat than rough surfaces, so that Wankel RC engines with machined epitrochoidal bore and rotor contour would seem to be favourably placed. Nor is there any difficulty in providing adequate surfaces for radiating the heat to the respective coolant round the outside. The problems are mainly confined to the development of a differential cooling system in accordance with the local heat transfer rates to the rotor housing. It is a great pity that the variation of heat input — from the gas to the rotor housing — per unit shown in Fig. 10.4 is non-dimensional. Accordingly various methods of circulating the cooling liquid have been devised to achieve a heat dissipation rate commensurate with the heat input. NSU seemed to prefer a substantially peripheral circulation for their KKM 502 single rotor engine Fig. 10.5, whereas Curtiss-Wright, and at least one other licensee, prefer a multi-pass axial flow arrangement, Fig. 10.6. Differential local transfer rates are possible with both systems by

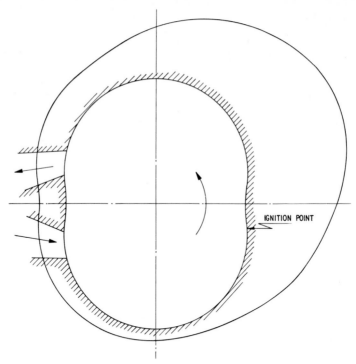

IGNITION POINT

Fig. 10.4. As induction, compression, expansion and exhaust are confined to their respective quarters of rotor movement, the heat transfer rate per unit bore area varies as shown. No actual values are shown because the figure illustrates the transfer rate of an experimental engine under full load and at the speed at which maximum power is developed

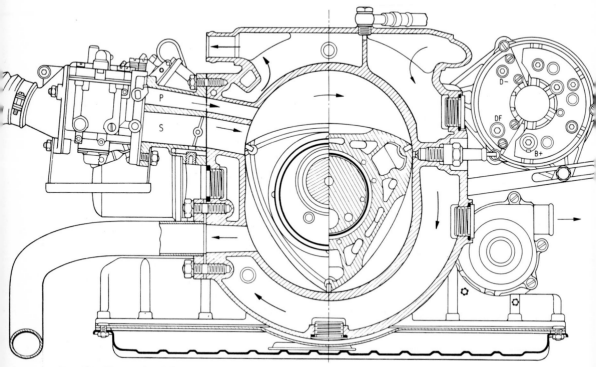

Fig. 10.5. The peripheral flow of coolant round the epitrochoidal bore of the KKM 502 engine is clearly seen, as are the primary (small) and secondary (large) inlet ports and the shrouded spark-plug

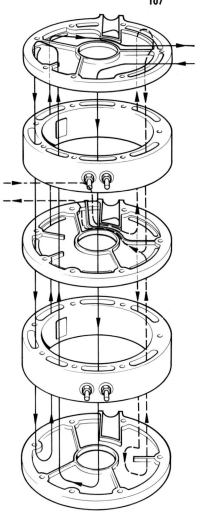

*Fig. 10.6. Multi-pass coolant flow arrangement of Toyo Kogyo liquid cooled twin rotor RC engine, which is in production for the Mazda Cosmo car. Temperatures round the housings are minimised by the controlled circulation of hot exhaust gases*

increasing the wetted area round the hot segment of the rotor housing and/or increasing the flow of coolant. It is, therefore, hardly a question of which is superior as long as the discussion concerns only single or twin rotor engines developing b.m.e.p. figures within the range of conventional piston engines. For multi-rotor and high performance engines it seems likely that peripheral flow round every rotor housing supplied from a common distribution pipe may ensure more equal rotor housing temperatures. Furthermore, if each rotor housing and end cover has an entirely independent circulation system the joints between them will have to ensure an adequate gas seal rather than provide gas and coolant sealing despite considerable temperature differences, and some unavoidable distortion. The remaining problems are associated with the sparking plug boss, the exhaust port and, of course, clamping together of rotor housings and end covers, which requires careful consideration during the design stages.

# 11

# Ignition

Although ignition is an indispensable prelude to the combustion process in Otto-cycle engines, it is opportune to divorce its consideration from the actual dynamics of combustion as different factors govern its performance and present their own peculiar problems. Apart from the time honoured magneto and coil ignition systems, all others are fairly recent developments – it is less than two decades since the transistor was invented. Today we can choose from six fundamentally different ignition systems, namely:

1. Magneto system
2. Coil Ignition system
3. Capacitor discharge ignition system ⎫ transistorised
4. Contact controlled ignition system ⎬ ignition
5. Magnetically controlled ignition system ⎭ systems.
6. Piezo-Electric ignition system

Inevitably the continuous and steady upward trend in engine performance in terms of speed, output and durability was to lead to the development of new ignition systems, unless an artificial horizon to engine development proved acceptable. It may be recalled in this connection that the original V16 1·5 litre **BRM** engine, which was designed for speeds of 16,000 rev/min, incorporated four distributors running at quarter engine speed. Every distributor contained two sets of contact breakers, one to break the primary circuit and the other to close it again – an expedient designed to overcome the limitations of the conventional contact breaker without sacrifice of reliability. Some of the latest electronic ignition systems are quite capable of sustaining reliably considerably higher speed without recourse to such complications. This is no slur on electrical equipment manufacturers who have, after all, enormously improved component durability and reliability under highly competitive conditions. Moreover, ignition systems are now being fitted to mass produced engines which, thirty years ago, were developed for peak performance racing engines, which is no mean achievement.

This evidence suggests that sufficient technical know-how and actual ignition systems are available to permit the attainment of even higher engine performance levels, which seems of particular significance for the Wankel RC engine because the spark plug(s) associated with every rotor must provide a spark of sufficient energy per shaft revolution, and on account of this engine's otherwise remarkable 'High Performance' potential.

Generally speaking the trend in automobile engineering is towards a reduction, if not elimination, of servicing requirements, that is various units such as joints, gearboxes, axles etc., lubricated for the expected life of the car. Yet spark plug and ignition system manufacturers still recommend checking and cleaning of plugs and points after every 5,000 miles, and replacement of the ignition plugs after every 10,000 miles if loss of power, starting difficulties in cold weather, or misfiring under some operating conditions are to be avoided. 10,000 miles represents up to about 250 hr engine running time, moreover the servicing requirements for vehicles running under the stop-go conditions of city traffic will be greater because these engines seldom reach the self-cleaning temperature of the spark plugs in time, so there is a much more pronounced tendency to form deposits.

Although the function of the spark plug is generally appreciated, it seems opportune to reiterate that combustion ought to occur under substantially constant volume conditions in any engine which depends upon intermittent-cyclic-combustion processes, and which includes, of course, the Wankel RC engine. To the ignition plug is assigned the important task of providing a source of energy to raise the temperature of a very localised spot within the chamber, and thereby initiating combustion. Once a burning nucleus has formed it will grow rapidly by a continuous process of heating up the mixture, layer by layer, so that the flame may propagate itself throughout the chamber. The rate of this heat conversion must, of course, exceed any heat losses which may occur at the same time. Despite the shortness of the actual combustion process it is obviously affected by numerous factors, including the temperature and energy release of the respective spark.

It is strange, therefore that so much exaggerated importance is attached only to the surface to volume ratio; great care must be exercised when comparing engine performance characteristics of different types of engines, especially in connection with the Wankel RC configuration.

Perhaps the most significant difference between conventional piston engines and the Wankel RC configuration is that the spark plug is not cooled to the same extent by the incoming fresh charge. It is usually located in the proximity of the minor axis, where the charge reaches it at some advanced stage during the compression phase, when its temperature is already considerably above ambient, partly due to compression and partly because it has had an opportunity to absorb heat from the rotor and the housing. Furthermore, the whole charge moves past the spark plug as explained in Chapter 8. With one complete thermodynamic cycle taking place during every shaft revolution—the shaft turning at three times rotor speed—it is obvious that one ignition occurs per shaft revolution. The ignition system has, therefore, a task very similar to that of a single cylinder two-stroke engine running at the same speed. Hence the Wankel RC engine requires spark plugs of relatively high heat rating despite any problems which might arise during cold starting, under part load operations and under overrun conditions.

NSU solved these problems on their KKM 502 RC engine by fitting a Bosch high tension condenser discharge ignition system, which produces adequate sparks even when the plug is fouled by deposits. In addition NSU and some licensees prefer to bring the discharge electrode close to the epitrochoidal surface, but provide only a $\frac{1}{8}$ in diameter hole — see Fig. 10.6 — for access to the chamber. The purpose of this arrangement is to minimise any gas blow-by from one chamber to the one adjacent, whilst an apex seal passes over the hole. Curtiss-Wright also developed a condenser discharge ignition system which produced a voltage rise four times that of a conventional ignition system, besides reducing any tendencies to gap erosion and fouling deposits.

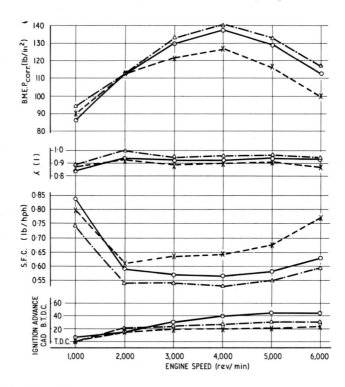

Fig. 11.1. The effects of spark plug location and of dual ignition on b.m.e.p., specific fuel consumption and on performance. Three conditions were investigated:

| x------------------x | spark plug placed 20 mm after minor axis |
| o----------------o | spark plug placed 28 mm before minor axis |
| —·—·—·—·—·—·— | one spark plug 56 mm before and the other 20 mm after minor axis |

Fichtel & Sachs, on the other hand, fit the same ignition system to their KM industrial RC engines as they fit to one of their small two-stroke engines. They found that a standard mo-ped spark plug — Bosch W 150 M11S — gives a satisfactory service life of 150–250 hr, which is comparable with the durability of a mo-ped spark plug. Although the tapped hole breaks right through into the epitrochoidal bore, blow-by of gases whilst an apex seal passes over the spark plug hole does not seem to cause any serious problems. It is interesting to note that the current re-appraisal of Wankel RC engine ignition has created an atmosphere favouring a return to more conventional coil ignition systems. Indeed the problems encountered are not fundamentally different from those of modern reciprocating

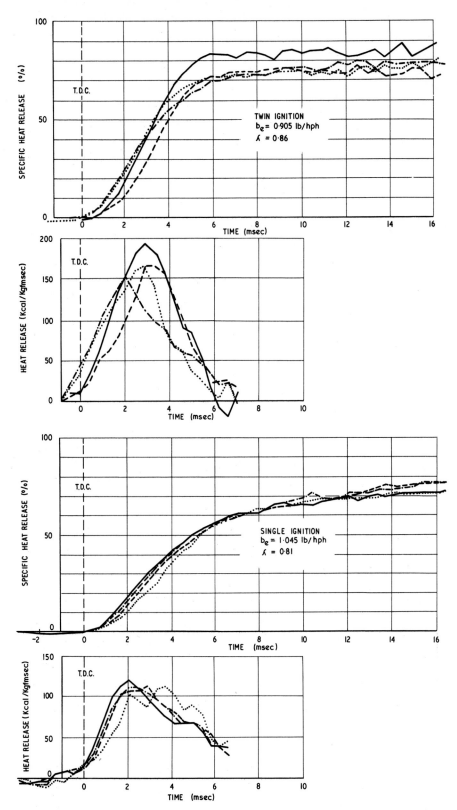

Fig. 11.2. Heat release and specific heat release of NSU/Wankel RC engine at 2,000 rev/min and under part load —
27.2 lb/in² b.m.e.p. conditions

piston engines, despite the fact that some problems are decidedly peculiar to the Wankel RC engine.

Dual ignition, shown in Figs. 11.1 and 11.2, that is two spark plugs per cylinder which fire simultaneously, has been applied to certain reciprocating piston engines to ensure greater reliability and, to a lesser extent, to raise power output. It is possible to coax a little more power from a Wankel RC engine with dual ignition because it speeds the whole combustion process, resulting in a more rapid pressure rise, and thus providing a longer effective expansion phase. The choice of spark plug location in conventional piston engines is more or less at the mercy of the valves, the ports and of the bolts or studs which secure the cylinder head to the cylinder block. By virtue of the comparatively long trochoidal bore surface between the respective apex seals when ignition is about to occur, the Wankel RC engine offers a considerably wider choice in spark plug position than its conventional counterpart and, in addition, it is eminently suitable for dual or multi-ignition should this commend itself.

When choosing the spark plug position or positions of Wankel RC engines it seems imperative to create the spark in such a position that the mixture contained between the depression in each rotor flank and the bore is directly ignited rather than the mixture in the relatively thin leading or trailing part of the chamber.

Locating the spark plug b.t.d.c. on engines with symmetrically disposed depressions on their rotor flanks ensures smoother performance than placing them in an a.t.d.c. position, though the latter slightly pushes up the power output. However, the b.t.d.c. spark plug position is the most widely used because this ensures more satisfactory ignition over the range of widely differing fuel/air ratios.

Since it is possible to fit more than one spark plug to every chamber housing of a Wankel RC engine, and already it is suggested that this type of engine can derive benefits from dual- or multi-ignition, it is pertinent to ask whether the plugs should discharge simultaneously or according to some purposeful predetermined pattern. In support of this contention it should be pointed out that the Mazda 110S RC engine relies upon a phased dual ignition system, the two plugs firing in sequence $2° - 7°$ a.t.d.c. at idling speed.

Unfortunately, multi- or dual-ignition also presents practical problems because the time lags between the sequential discharges amount necessarily to only a few diminishing microseconds as engine speed rises. It is, of course, possible to arrange that dual ignition is operative up to a certain speed, above which the engine reverts to single ignition. Indeed this is technically defensible, and is already under development for conventional reciprocating piston engines. The alternative of a virtually separate ignition system for each plug, may not be so attractive from an economic point of view. As indicated above, phased dual ignition systems, as opposed to the two separate ignition systems, prescribed for reciprocating piston aircraft engines are already under development. They point towards improved reciprocating piston and RC engine performance, as well as lower fuel consumption and more satisfactory exhaust emissions.

# 12

# Power Output

Since the rotor of a Wankel RC engine has three flanks, which are exposed to varying gas pressures, it may be assumed that three forces will be acting through the rotor centre, which coincides with the centre of the eccentric part of the output shaft. In the case of an engine, the largest of these forces is that due to the gas pressure over the combustion and expansion period, until the pressure drop due to opening the exhaust port allows the compression pressure on the adjacent rotor flank to acquire controlling influence. The three forces are the product of the gas pressure in the respective chambers multiplied by the effective rotor areas over which they act; that is, the areas stretching from apex seal to apex seal. For simplicity's sake it may be assumed that these areas remain constant and equal to $2R'B_c \sin 60 = \sqrt{3}R'B_c \ldots$ derived from Equation 6.20, so that the force $P$ exerted by pressure $p$ on any rotor flank becomes

$$P = \sqrt{3}R'B_c p \text{ (see Fig. 5.4)} \tag{12.1}$$

In reality, the effective rotor flank areas vary slightly because the contact line between the apex seals and the epitrochoidal bore moves continuously over an angle $\pm\phi$ whilst the rotor moves, but variations are small — even nil for some positions — and may, therefore, be disregarded for the time being.

By reading off and tabulating the respective pressures from an indicator diagram (Fig. 12.1) — conventional or polar — it is possible to calculate the forces $P$ which act on the eccentric in every position, and thus obtain the turning moment diagram (Fig. 5.5) for the particular operating conditions and engine speed, as is sometimes done for reciprocating piston engines.

The tabulated calculations are particularly useful in this connection since the centrifugal effects due to the rotation of the masses of the rotor, the eccentric part of the output shaft and of the coolant oil must also be taken into account. Furthermore, it must not be forgotten that the shaft speed is three times that of the rotor. It will, therefore, be an advantage to choose the increments of the shaft position, for which the turning moments are to be calculated, as divisible by three, say 15° or 9° etc., depending on the desired accuracy of the turning moment diagram.

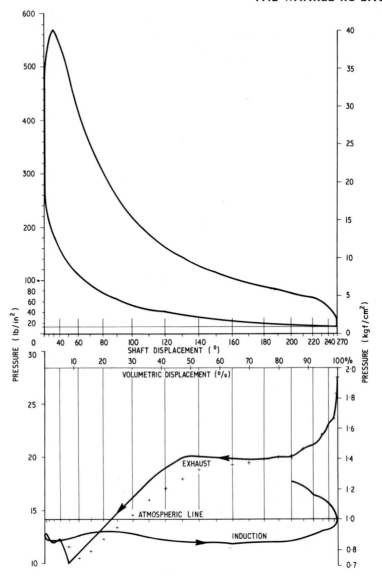

*Fig. 12.1. Typical indicator diagram of NSU/Wankel KKM 502 RC engine under full load at 5,000 rev/min*

The coolant within the rotor presents a problem as it circulates due to the centrifugal and centripetal forces acting on it. Moreover, the rotor cavities are only partly filled with cooling oil; in other words, in view of the relatively small mass of oil involved it seems permissible to disregard the effects of this small variable mass on the turning moment.

Before it is possible to calculate the turning moments for every rotor position it is, of course, essential to find the effective radius $r_e$ at which these forces are applied, assuming the minor axis to be the datum line from which the shaft displacement is measured is $3\alpha$.

$r_e$ = eccentricity × sin (shaft angle − rotor angle)

$$= e \sin (3\alpha - \alpha) \tag{12.2}$$

Defining the three variable forces as $P_1$, $P_2$ and $P_3$ which act on varying effective radii or moment arms

$$P_1, m_1 = e \sin 2\alpha$$

$$P_2, m_2 = e \sin \left(\frac{\pi}{3} - 2\alpha\right)$$

$$P_3, m_3 = e \sin \left(\frac{2\pi}{3} - 2\alpha\right) = e \sin \left(\frac{\pi}{3} + 2\alpha\right)$$

and torque due to gas pressures on rotor flanks of area $A$

$$= Ae \left[P_1 \sin 2\alpha + P_2 \sin \left(\frac{\pi}{3} - 2\alpha\right) - P_3 \sin \left(\frac{\pi}{3} + 2\alpha\right)\right]$$

as expected, this expression is cyclic with a period of $\frac{2\pi}{3}$ as is readily seen by adding $\frac{2\pi}{3}$ to $\alpha$, the expression becoming

$$Ae \left[P_1 \sin \left(2\alpha + \frac{4\pi}{3}\right) + P_2 \sin \left(\frac{\pi}{3} - 2\alpha - \frac{4\pi}{3}\right) - P_3 \sin \left(\frac{\pi}{3} + 2\alpha + \frac{4\pi}{3}\right)\right]$$

$$= Ae \left[P_1 \sin \left(\frac{\pi}{3} + 2\alpha\right) + P_2 \sin 2\alpha + P_3 \sin \left(\frac{\pi}{3} - 2\alpha\right)\right]$$

Note that Fig. 5.5 represents the torque fluctuations of single, twin, three and four rotor Wankel RC engines. As the effects of centrifugal force are small in comparison with the gas forces they were ignored.

Hence the tabulated calculations may be completed for a single rotor and a single shaft revolution, and the actual turning moment or torque fluctuation diagram may be plotted, see Fig. 5.5.

If the engine contains two or more rotors it is relatively easy to plot the torque fluctuation diagrams for all the other rotors and obtain the torque fluctuation diagram by simple mechanical summation of the various turning moments which act on the shaft in every position (see Fig. 5.5). The mean height of this diagram will be the mean torque of the engine over the whole phase, and its value may be inserted in the familiar power formula

$$\text{hp} = \frac{\text{Torque} \times 2\pi N}{33,000} \tag{12.3}$$

in which the torque is, of course, measured in lb ft and $N$ represents shaft revolution per minute. It may prove advantageous to compare Equation 12.3 with Equation 6.19 and see it reiterated once more that *the displacement volume is not a fundamental factor in the power formula.*

It is also interesting to note that whereas in reciprocating piston engines it is the inertia of the reciprocating masses which influences torque fluctation, it is the centrifugal force of the masses rotating about the output shaft centre which must be taken into account. Any balance weights attached to the shaft do not enter into this as they rotate with, and are part of, the shaft.

Centrifugal forces need only be considered if the centre of gravity of the rotor does not coincide with its geometric centre.

# 13

# Performance Characteristics

## 13.1. Fuel Requirements

Speculation about the minimum octane rating which the fuel of the Wankel RC engine must possess comes to the fore whenever this engine is discussed. So far it is known that, in common with the conventional engine, size effects demand a higher octane fuel for the larger Wankel RC engine than is required by smaller engines. However, the Wankel RC engine RC2-60-U5, as developed by the Curtiss-Wright Corporation specifically for automotive application, has a compression ratio of 8·9 to 1 and runs on regular grade petrol. Similarly Wankel-type RC engines as supplied by NSU, Fichtel & Sachs and others, run on regular grade gasoline (about 90 octane) despite their compression ratios of about 8·5 to 1 and above.

Independent tests have shown that Wankel RC engines are, in fact, not very demanding in the matter of the octane rating of their fuel. Indeed, an early experimental NSU/Wankel RC engine has run satisfactorily on 50 octane and even lower rated fuel.

## 13.2. Engine Noise and Vibrations

Irrespective of whether a twin or single rotor Wankel RC engine is installed in a car, it will make a decidedly different noise at idling speed and in the lower speeds than in the higher speed range, upward from 2,000 rev/min. In the lower ranges the exhaust note could perhaps be considered similar to that of a two-stroke engine, whilst in the higher speeds the noise level declines to the rhythmic purr of a perfectly tuned multi-cylinder engine. This change of sound from that at low to the more agreeable note in the higher speed ranges is accompanied by a notable fall in apparent engine roughness, particularly in the case of single rotor engines. This phenomena needs a little explanation as it is neither roughness in the accepted sense, nor can it be adequately described as vibration. Assuming a high idling speed of 900 rev/min, the rotor will be turning at only 5 rev/sec, and the noticeable phenomena are in fact the outward signs of the combustion process; these manifestations quickly die away as speed builds up, and they are barely perceptible in twin rotor engines. It could be said that, in a manner of speaking, the sensations of noise and vibration are opposite to those of reciprocating piston engines, which produce unmistakable outward signs when labouring in the higher speed and performance ranges. In the limit a missed gear can result in expensive damage to the cylinder head or crankcase, depending on whether a dropped valve or a connecting rod failure initiates a course of destruction.

These dangers are completely non-existent as far as Wankel RC engines are concerned, which is perhaps rather fortunate as the engine seems to respond more rapidly to throttle control and, unless care is practised, surprisingly high shaft speeds may be achieved

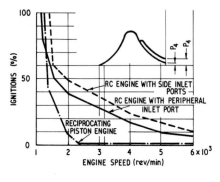

Fig. 13.1. Number of ignitions relative to engine speed observed under overrun conditions, i.e. engine braking

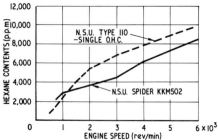

Fig. 13.2. Clearly, under overrun conditions, the Wankel RC engine has a lower hydrocarbon emission than the reciprocating piston engine down to nearly 1,200 rev/min

between gear changes and in the lower gears. For example an early NSU Spider car was taken round a test course inadvertently in second gear and with the engine exceeding 11,000 rev/min. This type of exuberance does not mean that irreparable damage has been done to the engine, little more than an early replacement of the apex seals is indicated, unless the condition prevailed long enough for chatter marks to develop on the epitrochoidal bore surface. These chatter marks will eventually affect performance, besides making the engine decidedly noisier, and require, therefore, a replacement of the centre housing in addition to new apex seals, unless it is more convenient to rework the surface.

Another engine performance phenomenon manifests itself under overrun conditions, which is in some respects an advantage. Dr. Ing. W. Froede found that, despite sparks, the mixture in an 1,100 $cm^3$ four-cylinder engine rarely ignited under overrun conditions until the engine speed had dropped to below 2,000 rev/min, the number of ignitions rising rapidly until 100% ignitions occurred at about 1,500 rev/min, Fig. 13.1. In the Wankel RC engine, the number of ignitions rose gradually from 6,000 rev/min, downward, reaching about 25%, i.e. one ignition every fourth shaft revolution at about 3,500 rev/min. It will be appreciated that these intermittent ignitions manifest themselves in the form of power impulses which the car occupants may feel as vibrations. The beneficial effects of these intermittent ignitions are, of course, a superior exhaust emission under overrun conditions (see Fig. 13.2), although the phenomenon suggests a remedy equally beneficial to reciprocating and Wankel RC engines, namely: complete interruption of fuel supply under overrun conditions, as is facilitated for example by the BRICO fuel injection system. Alternatively, it may be possible to minimise these effects by incorporating a hydrokinetic coupling or a torque converter, or perhaps a free-wheel in the transmission line, but these other remedies do not seem to go to the root of the problem.

It should be emphasised that this overrun problem was noticed on the road in one or two cars, the magnitude of the problem is not of such an order as might prejudice the whole Wankel RC engine project, as many motorists may not even be aware of what is happening.

## 13.3. Exhaust Emission

According to the preceding section the Wankel RC engine seems to offer a more satisfactory exhaust gas emission under overrun conditions than reciprocating piston engines (see Fig. 13.1) which rely upon carburettors, simply because there are, expressed in percentages, more actual ignitions over the whole speed range. This is more an incidental engine characteristic rather than a carefully nurtured tendency, and its manifestations were so far apparently more of an embarrassment than a blessing. Indeed, until a short while ago no particular efforts were made to investigate or improve exhaust emissions of Wankel RC engines as more fundamental performance and durability problems seemed to justify prior attention.

Before considering the exhaust emission characteristics of the Wankel RC engine it may be helpful to obtain a perspective of the broad general position of exhaust emissions, and where the Wankel RC engine stands relative to conventional engines.

G. R. Oliver of the Shell Company presented the findings shown in Fig. 13.3 at the 1965

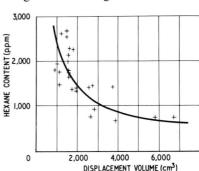

*Fig. 13.3. Hexane content of exhaust gases relative to the displacement volume (As shown by G. R. Oliver of Shell at the Champion Conference (1965)*

'Champion Ignition & Performance Conference', indicating a broad general relationship between hexane emissions and engine displacement.

Independent tests carried out in the U.S.A. and Great Britain have shown, according to Dr. Ing. W. Froede, that hexane emissions of the NSU/KKM502 engine, as fitted to the NSU Spider car, lie in the 1,400 to 1,600 p.p.m. range, which is undoubtedly rather high when compared with 275 p.p.m. specified at present in the Californian Test Procedure ($+1.5\%$ CO).

However, when comparing these emissions with those of equivalent displacement ($1,000 \text{ cm}^3$) reciprocating piston engines – the smallest included in the investigation – the emissions of the NSU/KKM 502 Wankel RC engine lie at the lower limit of the broad emission band of the reciprocating piston engines. Whilst this may be gratifying it is, by itself, no cause for rejoicing were it not for the portents which justify the belief that the devices developed for the control of exhaust emissions of conventional piston engines may, with equal effect, also be applied to the Wankel RC engine.

Although the subject of exhaust emissions is extraordinarily complex it seems worth-while to examine at least some of the factors which appear to have determining effects on exhaust emission. For instance, the surface/volume ratio is often quoted as a factor which permits comparison of the emissions of different engines. Let us see, therefore, whether this is a valid claim; combustion of the petrol-air mixture within any engine is by no means an instantaneous event, the flame is propagated from the ignition point at varying rates, depending, amongst other things, upon turbulence, the presence of petrol vapour, and even the size of the fuel particles suspended in the air. The flame is, in fact, completely quenched as it approaches the chamber walls, thus leaving a thin layer of unburned hydrocarbons, part of which mixes with and escapes with the products of combustion. It is contended that the amount of unburned hydrocarbon is proportional to the chamber surface area, and hydrocarbon emission may, therefore, be diminished by reducing the surface area. Despite an element of truth in this contention, it is evident that this is a gross over-simplification of the issues involved. To begin with, it is hardly possible to suggest that the hydrocarbon contents of this thin unburned layer will be the same irrespective of the richness or leanness of the mixture, as the thickness of this layer does seem to depend to some extent upon temperature – wall and mixture temperature – and flame propagation is known to increase with gas speed and/or turbulence. Accordingly it seems that the *least* significant factor is the surface area itself unless all other factors are neatly lined up, leaving the chamber surface as the only variable.

Reference has already been made to surface/volume relationship in Section 6.5, and comparisons have been made with reciprocating piston engines. Considering that the entire charge within a Wankel RC engine follows an orbital path and the transfer flow of gas from the trailing portion to the leading portion of the chamber, it does not seem reasonable to suggest that turbulence within the Wankel RC engine is of the same order as turbulence in any reciprocating piston engine. Moreover, *it seems justifiable to ask which is the significant surface area of the Wankel RC engine*, since the gases sweep over about half the trochoidal bore area and a portion of the end covers between the instance when ignition starts and exhaust is completed. Another equally pertinent question is

whether the chamber surface area at the beginning of combustion has the same significance as the chamber surface area at the beginning or end of the exhaust phase (see
Fig. 6.3 and Fig. 6.4).

Research has already revealed a practically linear relationship between the hexane
emission of the Wankel RC engine and engine temperature, see Fig. 13.4. Whether this

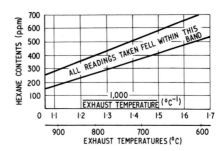

*Fig. 13.4. Within narrow limits the exhaust emission of Wankel*
*RC engines seems to depend upon exhaust temperature, whilst*
*no direct relationship between load and engine speed could*
*be established up to date*

also applies to reciprocating piston engines has not yet been proved, though it may
safely be assumed to have similar effects since higher thermal efficiency of any engine
may be achieved by either raising its compression ratio and/or its general running
temperature. However, it is known that more fuel must be supplied to a cold running
reciprocating piston engine to provide an air/fuel vapour ratio that will promote
combustion.

Undoubtedly there is room for cautious optimism that the efficiency of the combustion
process within the Wankel RC engine can be sufficiently improved over the whole broad
performance range of the engine so as to make any external aids for reducing noxious
exhaust emissions superfluous.

Furthermore, evidence suggests that the Wankel RC engine has a pronounced stratified
charge capacity, which depends strongly upon the orbital path of the charge prescribed
by the epitrochoidal bore. A stratified charge Wankel RC engine will probably have to
rely upon some form of direct fuel injection, hence the thin layer along the chamber
surface is unlikely to contain the same proportion of unburned hydrocarbons – if any –
as the carburettor engine. Similarly, the small pockets of each chamber, immediately
ahead of the trailing apex seal, are also unlikely to contain any significant amount of
unburned hydrocarbons.

In this connection it seems opportune to stress that comparison of exhaust emissions
of different engines are in themselves not very useful unless a combination of engine
performance characteristics and operating conditions are taken into account. After all,
the purpose is to protect the community as a whole against harmful emissions. For
instance, it cannot be denied that the exhaust emission of an engine, which runs for
considerable periods around 2,000 rev/min in city traffic has a different significance to
the same satisfactory emissions of an engine running at 2,000 rev/min, but whose
performance characteristics demand that under identical city traffic conditions it will
never be expected to run at less than 4,000 rev/min.

Fig. 13.5 was presented by Dr. Ing. W. Froede at his James Clayton lecture in

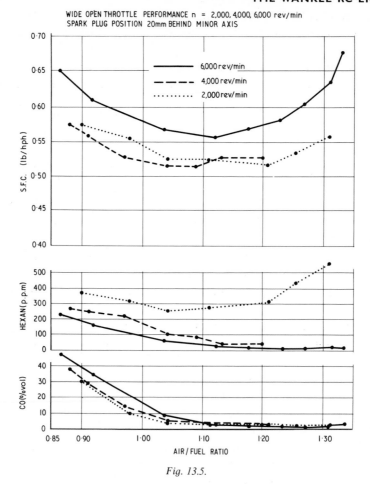

Fig. 13.5.

February 1966, it shows the relationship between specific fuel consumption (s.f.c.), hexane and CO emissions of the NSU KKM 502 RC engine relative to the fuel/air (F/A) ratio at various steady shaft speeds. It should be emphasised that although the development standard of this particular engine has long been superseded, its hexane emission need not shun comparison with equivalent reciprocating piston engines operating under the same conditions, nor should these preliminary figures be thought to represent in any way optimum values for the Wankel RC engine.

## 13.4. Performance

Figs 13.6–13.9 illustrate performance characteristics of four Wankel RC engines whose displacements vary between 108 cm$^3$ (6·6 in$^3$) and 2 × 980 cm$^3$ (2 × 59·6 in$^3$) per shaft revolution. Included are, for interest, the results of a preliminary investigation of performance in the higher speed range, which dates back to 1963, and was carried out with a single

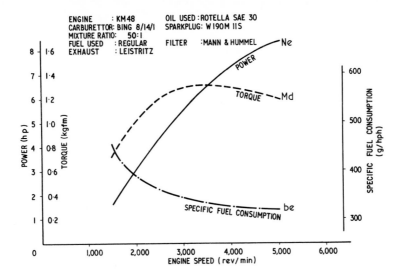

Fig. 13.6. Performance characteristics of Fichtel & Sachs KM37 single rotor Industrial Engine which displaces 108 cm³ per shaft revolution and has a compression ratio of 8·5 to 1

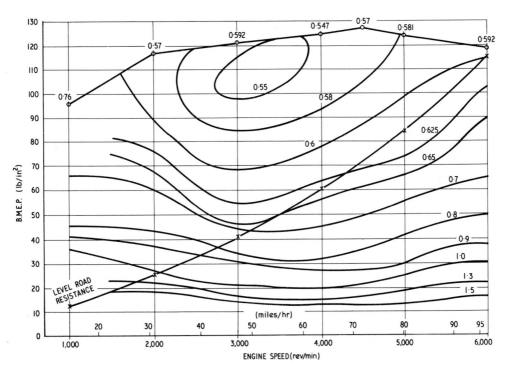

Fig. 13.7. Fuel consumption of NSU KKM 502 engine as well as the resistance encountered by the car and expressed as b.m.e.p.

rotor RC1-60 engine displacing 980 cm³ (59·8 in³) and specially adapted for this investigation. Of these engines only the NSU/Wankel KKM 502 and the Curtiss-Wright RC2-60-U5 were specifically developed for automotive applications. Both designs date back several years and have, of course, been overtaken by considerable developments aimed at better performance as well as improved specific fuel consumption, reliability and durability.

Evaluation of these full load performance curves with respect to those of reciprocating piston engines presents some problems despite their obvious similarity. Although comparisons may be odious, significant conclusions may perhaps be drawn by comparing the output torque characteristics upon an equitable non-dimensional basis. Figs. 13.10 and 13.11 show, therefore, torque curves expressed as percentages of maximum torque, and plotted with respect to percentages of maximum speed. Accordingly it will be noted that the reciprocating piston engines available for the purpose develop their maximum torque at 55, 62·2 and 75% of their maximum speed, whereas the Wankel RC engines develop their maximum torque at 50, 61·6, 65·8 and 74% of their respective maximum speeds. It is the droop of these curves on either side of the maxima which gains significance relative to other factors, such as car weight and minimum practical engine speed

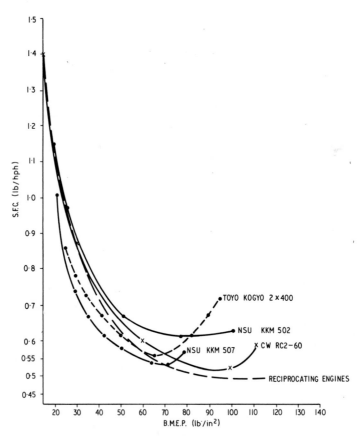

Fig. 13.8. Comparison of the specific fuel consumption of four different Wankel RC engines and a reciprocating piston engine

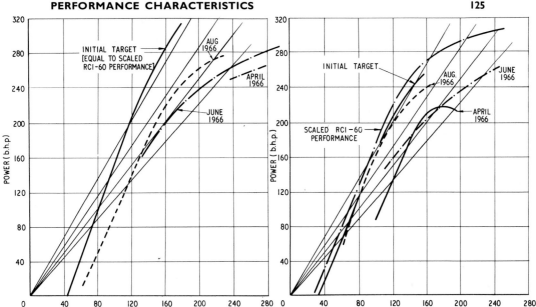

*Fig. 13.9. RC engine performance curve on JP and/or Diesel Fuel—from 'Design and Components'*

etc. For example, it was found that even in city traffic it was not possible to allow the engine speed of the sports car with the 800 cm³ (49 in³) engine to drop below 4,000 rev/min, if the engine was not to be stalled. This meant that not more than 50% of the entire speed range of the engine was available for practical purposes, and the torque developed from 50% maximum speed downward was of little practical value under normal driving conditions. On the other hand, driving the NSU Spider car under similar conditions showed that even at less than 30% of its maximum speed (≈ 2,000 rev/min) there was no imminent danger of stalling the engine, though below 35% the engine became decidedly lumpy. After all, a single rotor Wankel RC engine has only one power impulse per shaft revolution, which is the same as that of a twin cylinder four-stroke engine — see Fig. 6.8b.

It is, therefore, surprising that not only does this lumpiness vanish as engine speed rises, but the overall impression becomes a noticeable turbine-like smoothness with no audible indication when maximum permissible speed is approached. Be that as it may, it is far more difficult to elaborate on engine responsiveness as car acceleration figures are not entirely representative, since they reflect, amongst other things, that the correct gear ratios were chosen, they also reflect driver skill or well matched engine and torque converter characteristics and other factors.

In the absence of scientific data it may be assumed that most drivers appreciate the responsiveness of their cars; it may, therefore, be related that an experimental gas turbine powered car demonstrated a distinct lapse of time between the moment when the accelerator pedal was fully depressed and the beginning of noticeable acceleration. This phenomenon was of embarrassing proportions for city driving, and it was associated with the inertia of the rotating masses of the turbine power unit. Moreover, this feature is thought to be one of the fundamental problems of gas turbine powered cars. Impressive standing start acceleration figures are somewhat misleading because they are obtainable by revving up the turbine whilst hand and foot brakes are firmly applied; take off, with smoking tyres, occurs when the brakes are released.

The Chrysler Corporation and G.M.C. are reported to have been able to reduce these delay periods without discovering how they could be completely avoided. It is interesting to discuss these gas turbine characteristics with reference to Fig. 13.11, which emphasises that it is not torque but power that is required to accelerate the mass of the car. Far more interesting is the fact that, in this respect, the Wankel RC engine, and especially the

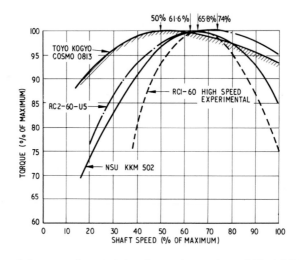

Fig. 13.10. Comparison of the torque characteristics of an early experimental Wankel RC engine and 3 engines intended for automotive evaluation. The curve for the TOYO KOGYO MAZDA COSMO 0813 twin rotor RC production engine was added as it illustrates that the Wankel RC engine is capable of having a superior torque characteristic to a wide range of conventional engines. cf. Fig. 13.11

NSU/KKM 502 and one or two pre-production twin rotor RC engines installed in cars, were decidedly more responsive. As already pointed out, no scientific data is available at present to confirm this impression, though experienced testers have reported that they feel it advisable to keep a watchful eye on the rev counter whilst in any indirect gear to avoid over-revving the engine until they have become familiar with the pitch of exhaust and gear noises at which gear changes ought to be made.

If, on occasions, the specified maximum engine speed is exceeded no catastrophe is imminent, though more rapid apex seal wear may be expected, and persistence in this practice may even lead to the formation of chatter marks on the epitrochoidal bore surface, which in severe cases affects engine noise and performance.

Independent testers in the U.S.A. have reported that a Ford Mustang car in which a Curtiss-Wright RC2-60-U5 engine was installed, not particularly well-matched with the torque converter characteristics, came within 0·6 sec of the official Ford figure of 10·6 sec given for accelerating the car from 0 to 60 m.p.h., whilst the acceleration from 25 to 70 m.p.h. was achieved in 12 sec, that is, only 1·5 sec in excess of the Ford figure. With all the test paraphernalia the car was 1¼ cwt heavier than the standard model and, in comparison with the Mustang's V8 engine, the RC engine developed about 8% less power, so that the performance is indeed most encouraging.

According to American opinion the RC engine could be built for $1 per b.h.p. compared

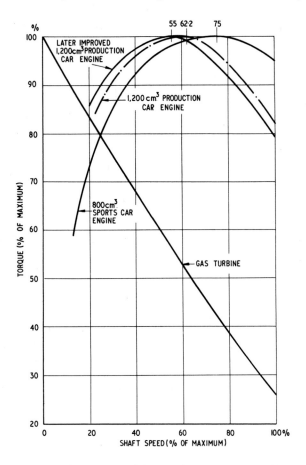

Fig. 13.11. Equally non-dimensional comparison of three production type car engines to which has been added a curve showing gas turbine characteristics. The high turbine torque at low shaft speed is, of course, of little practical value as efficiency is low and consequently little power becomes available for accelerating the vehicle

with nearly $2 per b.h.p. for current V8 piston engines. This favourable ratio diminishes as engine size comes down, nevertheless even small single rotor RC engines should cost less when produced at the same rate as equivalent power four-stroke reciprocating piston engines.

In view of what has already been said about the NSU KKM 502 RC engine, it is superfluous to emphasise any particular points, except perhaps to relate that quite a few users who have subjected their NSU Spider cars to very prolonged test programmes have commented favourably upon the low servicing requirements of the engine. They made less favourable remarks about inconsistent idling speeds and perhaps expected too much of the spark plugs, not to mention certain features of the Spider car; but, as a whole, there was wide agreement about the remarkably reliable and unobtrusive service of the latter's engines. Indeed, the reliability and durability standards achieved in other engineering fields seem to promise even better things from the Wankel RC engine in future, when production and materials experts have had the opportunity to concentrate upon specific problems or peculiarities of the Wankel RC engine.

## 13.5. Fuel Consumption

Next to power output and reliability, fuel consumption is undoubtedly of major interest, as it permits estimation of the cost of using the particular engine. Moreover, specific fuel consumption figures, usually specified in lb/b.h.p.hr, permit the comparison of different engines. The apparent anomaly of expressing the fuel consumption of cars in miles per gallon and specific fuel consumption in lb/b.h.p.hr, needs perhaps a word of explanation; the practice is quite reasonable as in one case it is endeavoured to appreciate the performance of a car, and in the other the fuel required for every brake horsepower developed by the engine — that is, the quality of the engine. The reason for specifying lb or g/b.h.p.hr is simply that the calorific value of every pound of fuel varies less than the calorific value of every pint or litre due to up to 10% difference in specific gravity of petrol. Reference has already been made to fuel properties in Section 10.1.

Fig. 13.7 gives a complete picture of the specific fuel consumption of the KKM 502 RC engine with respect to shaft rev/min, and m.e.p. In addition, the total resistance encountered by the Spider car at various speeds has been expressed as a 'b.m.e.p. required curve'.

Overall b.s.f.c. (brake specific fuel consumption) of four Wankel RC engines running at a steady 5,000 rev/min, are compared in Fig. 13.8 with the b.s.f.c. of a four-cylinder four-stroke engine with a swept volume of 1,000 cm³. It will be noticed that these curves extend over the lower b.m.e.p. range, i.e. up to 115 lb/in², which is, of course, the load range most widely used, especially by automotive installations. All the engines compared relied upon carburettors, and the fuel consumption of the NSU/KKM 502 RC engine is about 10% worse than that of the reciprocating piston engine. However, the b.s.f.c. of the experimental 2 × 400 cm³ and 2 × 1,000 cm³ engines, which were developed by licensees for automotive applications, show b.s.f.c. figures which are equal and, in fact, partly better than those of the particular conventional piston engine. It should perhaps be pointed out that the KKM 507 RC engine which was developed for industrial applications, maintains its superior fuel consumption over its entire load and speed range.

## 13.6. Fuel Injection

It would be wrong to exclude from this consideration most promising developments initiated at Curtiss-Wright in America, which were reported by Charles Jones in a paper presented to the Metropolitan Section, Society of Automotive Engineers, Farmingdale, Long Island, on November 3rd, 1966.

'Heavy-fuel versions of the basic carburetted engine are being developed by Curtiss-Wright. Fuel is directly injected into the combustion chamber by a high pressure diesel type nozzle located adjacent to the spark plug, and synchronised with the ignition timing. Unlike conventional low pressure intake manifold or early compression stroke-injection, this system is designed to accomplish all or most of the burning in a so-called "Stationary flame front" as it is injected. In practice, there are extraneous effects such as rotor surface evaporation and fuel carry-over, but combustion is effected largely as planned so that freedom from high octane rating and high volatility is achieved with a resultant capability to burn almost any liquid having realisable heating value. Best of all, this flexibility is accomplished with the same basic geometry ($R/e$ ratio) of our carburetted engines, so that the engine's compact size and capacity for high speeds are retained. The RC engine dynamics introduce inherent air transfer modes which form an ideal basis for this type of combustion. Engines of this type operate without inlet restriction or throttling since power is dictated by fuel addition; accordingly, they can be peripherally ported without the same low speed penalty as the carburetted engine. Thus the *RC spark ignited co-ordinated injection engine* enjoys the benefits of unthrottled part-load operation at low fuel-air ratios with the attendant savings of lower pumping losses; reduction of variable specific heat effects, dissociation and heat losses associated with higher temperatures; and lower exhaust temperatures. An interesting side effect may be a potentially cleaner exhaust than gasoline engines down at the 0·01–0·02 fuel air ratios possible for the light loads corresponding to much of automotive operation; measures have not yet been made, but if the excess air effects lead to anticipated results, the reduced number of injection units required per engine, coupled with the engine's low cost potential, may prove of interest in vehicle applications.

'On the other side, at least for a high performance machine, a penalty in output as compared to the carburetted gasoline engine is exacted by the task of having all of the injected fuel find the necessary air at peak outputs. The maximum specific output is about 20% less than a peripheral port carburetted engine at this stage. However, even with this penalty, the RC engines of this construction are very competitive, weight-wise, with other heavy fuel powerplants.' A representative performance is shown in Fig. 13.9.

It is thought that this advanced approach to fuel injection could lead to developments in RC engine applications far beyond those envisaged so far, and possibly transcending in importance the efforts under way to develop Diesel type Wankel RC engines. Of course, research into the thermodynamics of the Wankel RC engine is by no means confined to Curtiss-Wright in America, there is, for instance, very specific interest in the multi-fuel and stratified charge capability of the Wankel RC engine in Great Britain, whilst fuel injection is of special interest to several licensees throughout the world.

Whilst sifting data and writing this book it became apparent that, technically speaking, the Wankel RC engine has reached the application stage, which must not be construed to imply that no more problems remain to be solved. After all, the reciprocating piston engine has not reached that stage of perfection after nine decades of continuous development, and if it had, its days would indeed be numbered. Most important of all, the Wankel configuration seems to offer a potential far in excess of the capability of the reciprocating piston engine, though it will take time and patience to translate this potential into actual engines.

In a manner of speaking, it was perhaps unfortunate that so much effort was devoted to develop the Wankel RC engine over a performance and speed range at which it has to compete most fiercely with the highly sophisticated reciprocating piston engines of today. To have succeeded in this direction at all underlines the capability of the Wankel RC configuration and unstinted credit must be given to all those concerned.

It is realised that production problems have not been touched upon, which is deliberate since considerable efforts are being made at this very moment in Germany, Japan and the U.S.A. to find or evolve rational mass production techniques for some of the problem components or features of the Wankel RC engine configuration. It is not opportune to anticipate the outcome of these efforts, although there is no doubt that success is certain, since far more complex and difficult tasks have been successfully solved by production experts.

It is hoped that this book will assist many of those who have asked for a comprehensive exposition of Wankel RC engine design data. Many controversial points and issues have been elaborated, although the conclusions drawn may have to be revised in future, relative to later achievements due to deeper probing and development of specific features. As in most matters of human endeavour, it is better to have tried and failed than not to have tried at all.

# Appendix. Mathematical Analysis of the NSU Wankel RC Engine

## A.I. Generation of Trochoids

The family of curves traced out by points in the plane of a circle (the generating circle) which rolls without slipping on the circumference of a fixed circle (the base circle) are called trochoidal curves. Since the generating circle may roll either on the inside or the outside of the base circle or enclose it, it can be shown that where $a =$ radius of the generating circle and $b =$ radius of the base circle

1. Hypotrochoids are generated by rolling the generating circle inside the base circle with $a < b$.
2. Epitrochoids are generated either (a) by rolling the generating circle on the outside of the base circle with $a < b$, or (b) by rolling the generating circle on the outside of the enclosed base circle with $a > b$.

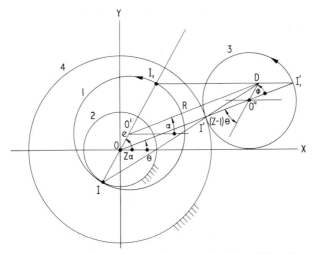

Fig. A1. The double generation of an epitrochoid For $O'D = R$, the following radius ratios can be proved:

$$\frac{R_1}{R_2} = \frac{R_3}{R_4} + 1; \quad \begin{array}{l} R_1 = R(1 + R_4/R_3) \\ R_2 = R(R_4/R_3) \end{array}$$

131

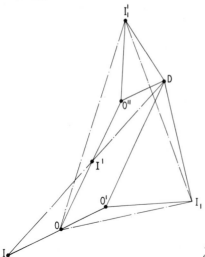

Fig. A2. Sylvester's skew pantograph. $OO'DO''$ is a parallelogram
and triangles $DO'I_1$, $DO''\,I'_1$ and $I_1\,I'_1\,O$ are similar

The multiple generation of trochoidal curves can readily be proved by the 'Belerman-Morley' theorem[1] and the double generation of an epitrochoidal path is illustrated in Fig. A.1. The generating circle 1 with centre $O'$ rolls on the outside of the fixed base circle 2 with centre $O$ and point $D$ fastened to circle 1 describes an epitrochoid ($a > b$). For an arbitrary point $D$ in the plane of the rolling circle 3 of radius $O''I' = R_3$ in contact with the base circle 4 of radius $OI' = R_4$, at $I'$ the instantaneous centre, the conditions for double generation of the path of $D$ are that $I$, $I'$ and $D$ are collinear and that $OO'DO''$ is a parallelogram where $O''$ lies on the extension of $OI'$ ($a < b$).

The parallelogram $OO'DO''$ and the similar triangles $DI'O''$ and $DO'I$ or $DI_1O'$ and $DO''I'_1$ then form a skew pantograph or plagiograph described by J. J. Sylvester[2] which is shown more generally in Fig. A.2.

For the trochoidal curves to be unicursal, however, the ratio $a:b$ must be the ratio of successive integers and clearly if the point $D$ in the plane of the generating circle lies on the circumference of this circle, the family of curves generated by this construction are the familiar cycloidal curves.

## A.2. Generation of Epitrochoids

In Fig. A.3, let

  $\alpha$ = The angle between the reference axis $PP'$ of the generating circle, $a$, and $XX'$ the reference axis of $b$, the fixed circle

  $\phi$ = The angle between the normal to the epitrochoid at $D$ and $O'D$ the generating radius of the rolling circle

  $\psi$ = The angle between the reference axis $XX'$ and $OI$ produced, the radius from the origin to the point of contact of the generating and fixed circles

  $\theta$ = The angle between the reference axis $PP'$ of the rolling circle and $OI$ produced

$\left.\begin{array}{l} XX' \\ YY' \end{array}\right\}$ = reference axes with respect to the fixed circle, radius $b = (Z-1)e$, centre $O$

$\left.\begin{array}{l} PP' \\ QQ' \end{array}\right\}$ = Reference axes with respect to the generating circle, radius $a = Ze$, centre $O'$

Since $A$ and $B$ are initially co-incident the condition for rolling contact is that

arc $AI$ = arc $BI$

i.e. $a\theta = b\psi$

or $Z\theta = (Z-1)\psi$                                   (A.1)

since $a = Ze$ and $b = (Z-1)e$

Now from Fig. A.3, $\theta + \alpha = \psi$

Substituting in Equation A.1 gives $Z\alpha = \psi$

Let $D$ be a point on $PP'$ such that $\overline{O'D} = R$

Hence the co-ordinates of $D$ with respect to the fixed axes $XX' - YY'$ are;

$$x = e \cos \psi + R \cos \alpha$$
$$y = e \sin \psi + R \sin \alpha$$

That is, $\left.\begin{array}{l} x = e \cos Z\alpha + R \cos \alpha \\ y = e \sin Z\alpha + R \sin \alpha \end{array}\right\}$                      (A.2)

By definition, the path of $D$ is an epitrochoid and in the special case where $\overline{O'D} = Ze = R$, the path of $D$ is an epicycloid.

Normally, the bore of a Wankel engine is increased over a true epitrochoid by a small distance normal to the epitrochoid to allow the sealing line to move across the radiused face of the apex sealing strip without subjecting it to any additional radial accelerations.

The actual bore is therefore a curve parallel to the epitrochoid by a distance $c$ as shown in Fig. A.3. The equations to this shape follow from Equations A.2 as follows:

$$\left.\begin{array}{l} x = e \cos Z\alpha + R \cos \alpha + c \cos (\alpha + \phi) \\ y = e \sin Z\alpha + R \sin \alpha + c \sin (\alpha + \phi) \end{array}\right\}$$         (A.3)

The difference between this curve and an epitrochoid where the generating radius $O'D = R + c$ is insignificant, particularly when compared with the distortions resulting from thermal effects and manufacturing errors.

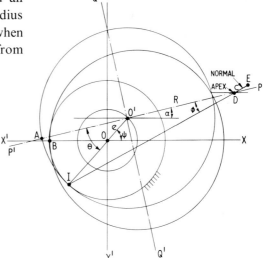

Fig. A3. Co-ordinate system for Trochoid generation

## A.3. The Parameter $\phi$

An important function which occurs frequently in the analysis is the angular relationship between the generating radius $O'D = R$ and the normal to the trochoid passing through the tracing point $D$ from the instantaneous centre $I$. Denoted by $\phi$, the apex obliquity measures the angle turned through by an apex seal relative to the normal to the curve. This angle will be shown to depend solely upon the ratio of $R:e$ but because of its relevance to the obliquity of the apexes it is a more useful parameter than the simple ratio of $R:e$.

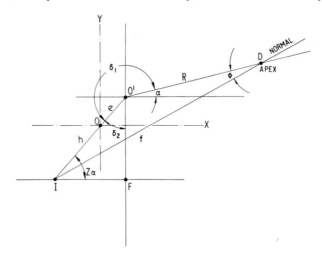

Fig. A4. Apex obliquity

Rather surprisingly $\phi$ also turns up in the evaluation of the working volume and the compression ratio since it determines the shape of the rotor. It will also be seen that $\phi$ is the angle between a tangent to the rotor at an apex and a perpendicular to the generating radius, and thus it gives an indication of the 'sharpness of the discontinuity' in the rotor profile at an apex. Fig. A.4, which is derived from Fig. A.3, shows the geometrical configuration used in evaluating $\phi$. Thus in $\Delta IO'F$,

$$\delta_2 = \frac{\pi}{2} - Z\alpha$$

but     $\delta_1 = 2\pi - \left(\delta_2 + \frac{\pi}{2} + \alpha\right)$

$\therefore$     $\delta_1 = \pi + (Z-1)\alpha$

and $\cos \delta_1 = -\cos (Z-1)\alpha$

Now     $f^2 = h^2 + R^2 - 2hR \cos (2\pi - \delta_1)$

or     $f^2 = h^2 + R^2 - 2hR \cos \delta_1$                    (A.4)

Similarly $h^2 = f^2 + R^2 - 2fR \cos \phi$

$\therefore$     $\cos \phi = \dfrac{R^2 + f^2 - h^2}{2Rf}$

Substituting for $f^2$ from Equation A.4,

$$\cos \phi = \frac{R - h \cos \delta_1}{[h^2 + R^2 - 2hR \cos \delta_1]^{\frac{1}{2}}}$$

Hence $\cos \phi = \dfrac{R + h \cos (Z - 1)\alpha}{[h^2 + R^2 + 2hR \cos (Z - 1)\alpha]^{\frac{1}{2}}}$ \hfill (A.5)

which may be written;

$$\phi = \text{arc cos} \frac{R + h \cos (Z - 1)\alpha}{[h^2 + R^2 + 2hR \cos (Z - 1)\alpha]^{\frac{1}{2}}} \hfill \text{(A.6)}$$

that is, $\phi = \text{arc cos } f(\alpha)$

Hence, since $\dfrac{d}{d\alpha}[\text{arc cos } f(\alpha)] = \dfrac{-1}{[1 - f(\alpha)^2]^{\frac{1}{2}}} \dfrac{df(\alpha)}{d\alpha}$

for $0 \leqslant \text{arc cos } f(\alpha) \leqslant \pi$,

it follows that;

$$\frac{d\phi}{d\alpha} = -\frac{[R^2 + h^2 + 2hR \cos (Z - 1)\alpha]^{\frac{1}{2}}}{h \sin (Z - 1)\alpha} \frac{df(\alpha)}{d\alpha}$$

and therefore;

$$\frac{d\phi}{d\alpha} = \frac{2h[h + R \cos (Z - 1)\alpha]}{h^2 + R^2 + 2hR \cos (Z - 1)\alpha} \hfill \text{(A.7)}$$

Now $\dfrac{d\phi}{d\alpha} = 0$, when $[h + R \cos (Z - 1)\alpha] = 0$

that is, when $\cos (Z - 1)\alpha = -\dfrac{h}{R}$

Substituting for $\cos (Z - 1)\alpha$ in Equation A.5,

$$\cos \phi_{max} = \frac{(R^2 - h^2)^{\frac{1}{2}}}{R} \hfill \text{(A.8)}$$

Hence $\sin \phi_{max} = \dfrac{h}{R}$

Since $h = Ze$,

$$\sin \phi_{max} = \frac{Ze}{R} \hfill \text{(A.9)}$$

The rate of change of apex seal obliquity with time follows from Equation A.7, since

$$\frac{d\phi}{dt} = \frac{d\phi}{d\alpha} \cdot \frac{d\alpha}{dt}$$

$$\therefore \quad \frac{d\phi}{dt} = \frac{2h[h+R\cos(Z-1)\alpha]\omega}{h^2+R^2+2hR\cos(Z-1)\alpha} \qquad\qquad (A.10)$$

From this expression the local variation in the velocity of the apex sealing line can readily be deduced.


## A.4. The Envelope of a Trochoid

The envelope of the trochoid is generated by rigidly attaching the epitrochoid concentrically to the base circle radius $b$ and rolling this circle and the attached trochoid round the inside of the previous generating circle of radius $a$, which is now fixed at centre $S$ $(OS = e)$.

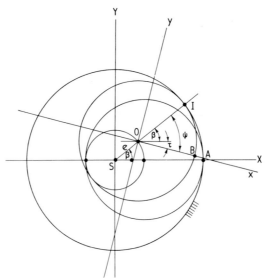

Fig. A5. Development of the envelopes to the general trochoid

In Fig. A.5, let $SX$–$SY$ be a fixed system of axes and let $O$ be the centre of the generating circle, radius $b$.

Let $Ox$–$Oy$ be a system of axes fixed with respect to the rolling circle and $I$ be the point of contact between the circles or the instantaneous centre.

Then, since $A$ and $B$ are initially coincident, the condition for rolling contact is arc $AI$ = arc $BI$

i.e.       $a\beta = b\psi$

But from the figure, $\beta + \tau = \psi$

$\therefore \qquad b\tau = (a-b)\beta$

i.e. $\qquad \tau = \dfrac{(a-b)\beta}{b}$

Since $a = Ze$ and $b = (Z-1)e$,

$$\tau = \frac{\beta}{(Z-1)} \qquad \text{(A.11)}$$

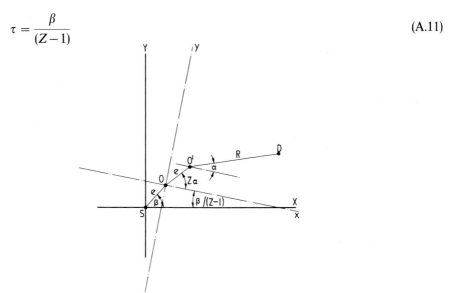

Fig. A6. Co-ordinate system for envelopes to the general trochoid

Fig. A.6 follows from Fig. A.5 and the above discussion. Consider a point $D$ in Fig. A.6 lying on the trochoid; in the $x$, $y$ axis system, $D\ (x, y)$ is the point

$$\left. \begin{array}{l} x = e \cos Z\alpha + R \cos \alpha \\ y = e \sin Z\alpha + R \sin \alpha \end{array} \right\} \qquad \text{(A.2)}$$

From Fig. A.6, the co-ordinates of $D$ in the $X$, $Y$ plane are given by

$X = e \cos \beta + e \cos [Z\alpha - \beta/(Z-1)] + R \cos [\alpha - \beta/(Z-1)]$
$Y = e \sin \beta + e \sin [Z\alpha - \beta/(Z-1)] + R \sin [\alpha - \beta/(Z-1)]$
Let $\beta = u - Zv$
and $Z\alpha - \beta/(Z-1) = u + Zv$
then $\alpha - \beta/(Z-1) = (u+Zv)/Z - (u-Zv)/Z = 2v$

Therefore the co-ordinates of $D$ become;

$X = e \cos (u - Zv) + e \cos (u + Zv) + R \cos 2v$
$Y = e \sin (u - Zv) + e \sin (u + Zv) + R \sin 2v$
or $\quad \left. \begin{array}{l} X = 2e \cos u \cos Zv + R \cos 2v \\ Y = 2e \sin u \cos Zv + R \sin 2v \end{array} \right\} \qquad \text{(A.12)}$

The envelope curve of the trochoid is generated by points of intersection of consecutive curves as the angle $v$ is varied. This will be illustrated by Taylor's Theorem as follows.

Let $f(x, y, c) = 0$ be the equation to a parametic system or family of curves, where individual curves are derived by assigning particular values to the parameter $c$.

A curve which is a neighbour to the curve $f(x, y, c) = 0$ has the equation $f(x, y, c+\Delta c) = 0$, where $\Delta c$ is a small increment of $c$. By Taylor's Theorem,

$$f(x, y, c+\Delta c) = f(x, y, c) + \frac{\partial}{\partial c}[f(x, y, c)]\Delta c + \frac{1}{2}\frac{\partial^2}{\partial c^2}[f(x, y, c+\theta\Delta c)].(\Delta c)^2$$

where $0 < \theta < 1$.

At points of intersection of the curves, where $f(x, y, c) = 0$ and $f(x, y, c+\Delta c) = 0$, this equation becomes:

$$\frac{\partial}{\partial c}[f(x, y, c)] + \frac{1}{2}\frac{\partial^2}{\partial c^2}[f(x, y, c+\theta\Delta c)](\Delta c) = 0$$

As $\Delta c \to 0$, a point of intersection of the curves tends to a point which satisfies both

$$f(x, y, c) = 0 \text{ and } \frac{\partial f}{\partial c}(x, y, c) = 0$$

Such limiting points are called points of intersection of 'consecutive' curves of the system and the locus of these points as $c$ varies, is the envelope of the system of curves.

In this case, the points on the envelope satisfy Equations A.12, together with the further conditions:

$$\left.\begin{array}{l} \dfrac{dX}{dv} = 0 \\[3mm] \dfrac{dY}{dv} = 0 \end{array}\right\} \qquad\qquad\text{(A.13)}$$

Since $X$ and $Y$ are functions of both $u$ and $v$,

$$\frac{dX}{dv} = \frac{\partial X}{\partial v} + \frac{\partial X}{\partial u}\cdot\frac{du}{dv}$$

$$\frac{dY}{dv} = \frac{\partial Y}{\partial v} + \frac{\partial Y}{\partial u}\cdot\frac{du}{dv}$$

From Equations A.12 and A.13

$$\frac{dX}{dv} = -2Ze\cos u \sin Zv - 2R\sin 2v - 2e\sin u\cos Zv.\frac{du}{dv} = 0$$

$$\frac{dY}{dv} = -2Ze\sin u\sin Zv + 2R\cos 2v + 2e\cos u\cos Zv.\frac{du}{dv} = 0$$

Multiplying by sin $u$ and cos $u$ to eliminate $\dfrac{du}{dv}$ gives

$Ze \sin Zv + R \sin 2v \cos u - R \cos 2v \sin u = 0$
which is of the form: $P + M \sin u + N \cos u = 0$
where $P = Ze \sin Zv$
$\qquad M = -R \cos 2v$
$\qquad N = R \sin 2v$

From which, it follows that:

$$\sin u = \frac{Ze}{R} \sin Zv \cos 2v \pm \left[ 1 - \left( \frac{Ze}{R} \right)^2 \sin^2 Zv \right]^{\frac{1}{2}} \sin 2v$$

and $\cos u = -\dfrac{Ze}{R} \sin Zv \sin 2v \pm \left[ 1 - \left( \dfrac{Ze}{R} \right)^2 \sin^2 Zv \right]^{\frac{1}{2}} \cos 2v$

Substituting the above relationships in Equations A.12 gives the envelope curve as;

$$X = R \cos 2v - \frac{Ze^2}{R} \sin 2Zv \sin 2v \pm 2e \left[ 1 - \left( \frac{Ze}{R} \right)^2 \sin^2 Zv \right]^{\frac{1}{2}} \cos 2v \cos Zv$$

and

$$Y = R \sin 2v + \frac{Ze^2}{R} \sin 2Zv \cos 2v \pm 2e \left[ 1 - \left( \frac{Ze}{R} \right)^2 \sin^2 Zv \right]^{\frac{1}{2}} \sin 2v \cos Zv$$

(A.14)

For the NSU-Wankel engine where $Z = 3$, the envelope is given by

$$X = R \cos 2v - \frac{3e^2}{R} \sin 6v \sin 2v \pm 2e \left[ 1 - \frac{9e^2}{R^2} \sin^2 3v \right]^{\frac{1}{2}} \cos 3v \cos 2v$$

and

$$Y = R \sin 2v + \frac{3e^2}{R} \sin 6v \cos 2v \pm 2e \left[ 1 - \frac{9e^2}{R^2} \sin^2 3v \right]^{\frac{1}{2}} \cos 3v \sin 2v$$

(A.15)

As $v$ varies from 0 to $2\pi$, the smooth curve generated by the parametric Equations A.15 above has three distinct nodes. The profile of the rotor which corresponds to the *inner* envelope is given by the portions of the curve from

$$v = \frac{\pi}{6} \text{ to } \frac{\pi}{2}, \frac{5\pi}{6} \text{ to } \frac{7\pi}{6} \text{ and } \frac{3\pi}{2} \text{ to } \frac{11\pi}{6} ;$$

the apexes of the rotor lying at these nodes.

## A.5. The Area of the General Rotor

The parametric equations of the rotor may be written as;

$$X = R\cos 2v - \frac{Ze^2}{R}\sin 2Zv \sin 2v + w\cos 2v$$

$$Y = R\sin 2v + \frac{Ze^2}{R}\sin 2Zv \cos 2v + w\sin 2v$$

where $w = 2e\left[1 - \left(\frac{Ze}{R}\right)^2 \sin^2 Zv\right]^{\frac{1}{2}}\cos Zv$

The area of any sector of the rotor between adjacent apexes is given by

$$\frac{1}{2}\int_{v_1}^{v_2} r^2 dv$$

or $\quad \frac{1}{2}\int_{v_1}^{v_2}\left(X\frac{dY}{dv} - Y\frac{dX}{dv}\right)dv$ $\hspace{3cm}$ (A.16)

where $v_1 = \frac{\pi}{2Z}$ and $v_2 = \frac{3\pi}{2Z}$

Substituting in Equation A.16 and collecting terms leads to the following integral for the area of the sector of a rotor

$$A = \int_{\frac{\pi}{2Z}}^{\frac{3\pi}{2Z}} \{R^2 + 2e^2 + (Z^2 + 2)e^2 \cos 2Zv +$$

$$\left[1 - \frac{(Ze)^2}{R^2}\sin^2 Zv\right]^{\frac{1}{2}}\cos Zv\left[4eR + \frac{2Z^2e^3}{R}(\cos 2Zv + \sin^2 Zv)\right]$$

$$+ \left[1 - \frac{(Ze)^2}{R^2}\sin^2 Zv\right]^{-\frac{1}{2}}\cos Zv\left(\frac{Z^4e^5}{R^3}\sin 2Zv \sin Zv \cos Zv\right)\} dv \hspace{1cm} (A.17)$$

The expression is integrated using the substitution $(Ze/R)\sin Zv = \sin\phi$. This changes the limits from $\pi/2Z$ to $\phi_{max}$ and $3\pi/2Z$ to $-\phi_{max}$

where $\phi_{max} = \arcsin\dfrac{Ze}{R}$ (see Equation A.9).

The value of the integral is found to be

$$A = (R^2 + 2e^2)\frac{\pi}{Z} - \frac{6eR}{Z}\cos\phi_{max} - \left(\frac{2R^2}{Z^2} + 4e^2\right)\phi_{max} \hspace{1cm} (A.18)$$

Thus the total area of a Z-flanked rotor (since it contains Z sections) is

$$A = (R^2 + 2e^2)\,\pi - 6eR\cos\phi_{max} - \left(\frac{2R^2}{Z} + 4e^2 Z\right)\phi_{max} \tag{A.19}$$

For the NSU Wankel engine where $Z = 3$, the area of a rotor is given by:

$$A = (R^2 + 2e^2)\,\pi - 6eR\cos\phi_{max} - \left(\frac{2R^2}{3} + 12e^2\right)\phi_{max} \tag{A.20}$$

## A.6. The Area Bounded by the Epitrochoid and the Apexes of a Rotor

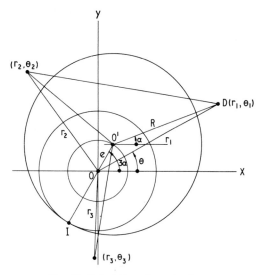

Fig. A7. Calculation of swept volume

The area of a sector bounded by the epitrochoid and the radial lines $r_1$ and $r_2$ in Fig. A.7 is given by

$$A = \tfrac{1}{2}\int_{\theta_1}^{\theta_2} r^2 d\theta$$

$$= \tfrac{1}{2}\int_{\alpha_1}^{\alpha_2} r^2 \left(\frac{d\theta}{d\alpha}\right) d\alpha$$

Substituting from Equation A.40 for $\dfrac{d\theta}{d\alpha}$ gives

$$A = \tfrac{1}{2}\int_{\alpha_1}^{\alpha_2} (3e^2 + R^2 + 4eR\cos 2\alpha)\,d\alpha$$

$$= \left[ (3e^2 + R^2)\frac{\alpha}{2} + eR \sin 2\alpha \right]_{\alpha_1}^{\alpha_2}$$

$$= \tfrac{1}{2}(3e^2 + R^2)(\alpha_2 - \alpha_1) + eR(\sin 2\alpha_2 - \sin 2\alpha_1)$$

But $(\alpha_2 - \alpha_1) = \dfrac{2\pi}{3}$

$$\therefore \quad A = (3e^2 + R^2)\frac{\pi}{3} + 2eR \cos 2\left(\alpha_1 + \frac{\pi}{3}\right)\sin\frac{2\pi}{3} \qquad\qquad \text{(A.21)}$$

[Similarly the total enclosed area of a unicursal epitrochoid is $\pi(3e^2 + R^2)$]

From the area of the sector it is necessary to deduct the area of the triangle $0r_1r_2$.
The area of the triangle $0r_1r_2 = \tfrac{1}{2}r_1r_2 \sin(\theta_2 - \theta_1)$

$$= \tfrac{1}{2}r_1r_2(\sin\theta_2 \cos\theta_1 - \sin\theta_1 \cos\theta_2)$$
$$= \tfrac{1}{2}(x_1y_2 - y_1x_2)$$
$$= \tfrac{1}{2}[(e\cos 3\alpha_1 + R\cos\alpha_1)(e\sin 3\alpha_2 + R\sin\alpha_2)$$
$$\quad - (e\sin 3\alpha_1 + R\sin\alpha_1)(e\cos 3\alpha_2 + R\cos\alpha_2)]$$
$$= \tfrac{1}{2}[e^2 \sin 3(\alpha_2 - \alpha_1) + R^2 \sin(\alpha_2 - \alpha_1) + 2eR \sin 2(\alpha_2 - \alpha_1)\cos(\alpha_2 + \alpha_1)]$$

But $\quad (\alpha_2 - \alpha_1) = \dfrac{2\pi}{3}$

$$\therefore \quad \Delta 0r_1r_2 = \frac{R^2}{2}\sin\frac{2\pi}{3} - eR\sin\frac{2\pi}{3}\cdot\cos 2\left(\alpha_1 + \frac{\pi}{3}\right) \qquad\qquad \text{(A.22)}$$

The area bounded by the epitrochoid and the apexes of the rotor is therefore

$$(A - \Delta 0r_1r_2) = (3e^2 + R^2)\frac{\pi}{3} + 2eR\cos 2\left(\alpha_1 + \frac{\pi}{3}\right)\sin\frac{2\pi}{3}$$

$$- \frac{R^2}{2}\sin\frac{2\pi}{3} + eR\sin\frac{2\pi}{3}\cos 2\left(\alpha_1 + \frac{\pi}{3}\right)$$

which reduces to the following expression.

$$\text{Bounded area} = (3e^2 + R^2)\frac{\pi}{3} - \frac{R^2}{2}\sin\frac{2\pi}{3} + 3eR\sin\frac{\pi}{3}\cos 2\left(\alpha_1 + \frac{\pi}{3}\right) \qquad \text{(A.23)}$$

The additional area $C$ between the triangle $0r_1r_2$ and the actual rotor profile between apexes must be subtracted from the expression above to give the total area and hence the volume of a chamber at any rotor angle $\alpha_1$.

It follows from above, that the maximum and minimum areas occur when
$\cos 2(\pi/3 + \alpha_1) = \pm 1$.

That is, when $(\pi/3 + \alpha_1) = n\pi$, $(n = 0, \pm 1, \pm 2$, etc.) for a maximum area, or when $(2\pi/3 + 2\alpha_1) = (2n + 1)\pi$, $(n = 0, \pm 1, \pm 2$, etc.) for a minimum area.

The maximum and minimum areas are therefore

$$A_{max,\ min} = (3e^2 + R^2)\frac{\pi}{3} - \frac{R^2}{2}\sin\frac{2\pi}{3} \pm 3eR\sin\frac{\pi}{3} - C \tag{A.24}$$

The area swept by a rotor flank during each revolution of the eccentric crank is therefore given by (maximum area − minimum area) $= 6eR\sin\pi/3$.

$$A_{swept} = 3\sqrt{3}Re \tag{A.25}$$

It will be seen that the actual shape of the rotor does not influence the area swept out by a rotor flank.

If the width of the rotor is $b$, the volume displaced during each revolution of the eccentric crank by each flank is $3\sqrt{3}Reb$. It follows that the theoretical compression

$$\text{ratio} = \frac{\text{Maximum area} - C}{\text{Minimum area} - C}.$$

i.e.
$$\varepsilon_{theo} = \frac{(3e^2 + R^2)\dfrac{\pi}{3} - \dfrac{R^2\sqrt{3}}{4} + \dfrac{3\sqrt{3}}{2}Re - C}{(3e^2 + R^2)\dfrac{\pi}{3} - \dfrac{R^2\sqrt{3}}{4} - \dfrac{3\sqrt{3}}{2}Re - C}$$

$$\therefore \quad \varepsilon_{theo} = \frac{e^2\pi + \dfrac{3\sqrt{3}}{2}Re + R^2\left(\dfrac{\pi}{3} - \dfrac{\sqrt{3}}{4}\right) - C}{e^2\pi - \dfrac{3\sqrt{3}}{2}Re + R^2\left(\dfrac{\pi}{3} - \dfrac{\sqrt{3}}{4}\right) - C} \tag{A.26}$$

The area of the inscribed equilateral triangle bounded by the apexes of the rotor is

$$\frac{3\sqrt{3}R^2}{4}.$$

Hence from Equation A.20 the difference in area between the rotor and the equilateral triangle is

$$\left[ (R^2 + 2e^2)\pi - 6eR\cos\phi_{max} - \left(\frac{2R^2}{3} + 12e^2\right)\phi_{max} - \frac{3\sqrt{3}R^2}{4} \right]$$

and hence $C = \dfrac{\pi}{3}(R^2 + 2e^2) - 2eR\cos\phi_{max} - 2\phi_{max}\left(\dfrac{R^2}{9} + 2e^2\right) - \dfrac{R^2\sqrt{3}}{4}$ \tag{A.27}

$\therefore$ The theoretical compression ratio is then given by

$$\varepsilon_{theo} = \frac{\dfrac{\pi e^2}{3} + 2eR\cos\phi_{max} + 2\phi_{max}\left(\dfrac{R^2}{9} + 2e^2\right) + \dfrac{3\sqrt{3}}{2}Re}{\dfrac{\pi e^2}{3} + 2eR\cos\phi_{max} + 2\phi_{max}\left(\dfrac{R^2}{9} + 2e^2\right) - \dfrac{3\sqrt{3}}{2}Re} \tag{A.28}$$

## A.7. Velocities and Accelerations

One of the most important factors in the NSU/Wankel engine is the interaction between
the apex sealing elements, and the stator bore. To analyse the motion of these sealing
elements, the mechanism is reduced to the linkage shown in Fig. A.8.

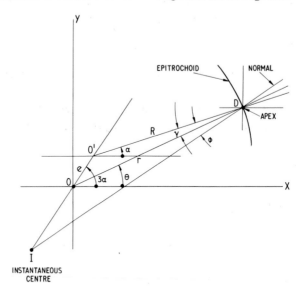

*Fig. A8. Co-ordinate system*

The eccentric crank is pivoted at the fixed point $O$, the centre of the epitrochoidal bore
and the crank and piston are hinged together at $O'$, the centre of the piston. Link $OO'$
of length $e$ represents the eccentricity of the crank and link $O'D$ if length $R$ represents the
generating radius of the epitrochoid. The system is constrained to move in a plane and
the inclinations of $OO'$, $O'D$ and $OD$ to $OX$ are denoted by $3\alpha$, $\alpha$ and $\theta$, respectively, at
time $t$. The angular velocity and acceleration of the piston are denoted by $\omega = d\alpha/dt$
and $\dot{\omega} = d^2\alpha/dt^2$ respectively.

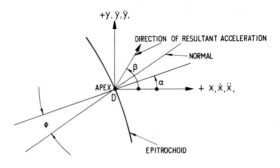

*Fig. A9. Sign convention*

The parametric equations of the tracing point or apex $D$ in Fig. A.8 are given by

$$\left.\begin{array}{l} x = e \cos 3\alpha + R \cos \alpha \\ y = e \sin 3\alpha + R \sin \alpha \end{array}\right\} \tag{A.2}$$

Hence the velocity of the apex along the epitrochoid $v = (\dot{x}^2 + \dot{y}^2)^{\frac{1}{2}}$ (A.29)

where $\dot{x} = \dfrac{dx}{dt} = \dfrac{dx}{d\alpha} \cdot \dfrac{d\alpha}{dt}$

and $\quad \dot{y} = \dfrac{dy}{dt} = \dfrac{dy}{d\alpha} \cdot \dfrac{d\alpha}{dt}$

Now $\quad \dot{x} = -\omega\,(3e \sin 3\alpha + R \sin \alpha)$  
and $\quad \dot{y} = +\omega\,(3e \cos 3\alpha + R \cos \alpha)$ $\left.\right\}$ (A.30)

$\therefore \qquad v = \omega\,(9e^2 + R^2 + 6eR \cos 2\alpha)^{\frac{1}{2}}$ (A.31)

The maximum and minimum velocities are therefore $v = \omega(3e \pm R)$
The acceleration of an apex is given by

$$A = (\ddot{x}^2 + \ddot{y}^2)^{\frac{1}{2}} \tag{A.32}$$

Where $\ddot{x} = \dfrac{d}{dt}\left(\dfrac{dx}{dt}\right) = \dfrac{dx}{d\alpha} \cdot \dfrac{d^2\alpha}{dt^2} + \left(\dfrac{d\alpha}{dt}\right)^2 \cdot \dfrac{d^2x}{d\alpha^2}$

and $\quad \ddot{y} = \dfrac{d}{dt}\left(\dfrac{dy}{dt}\right) = \dfrac{dy}{d\alpha} \cdot \dfrac{d^2\alpha}{dt^2} + \left(\dfrac{d\alpha}{dt}\right)^2 \cdot \dfrac{d^2y}{d\alpha^2}$

Now $\quad \ddot{x} = -\omega^2(9e \cos 3\alpha + R \cos \alpha) - \dot{\omega}(3e \sin 3\alpha + R \sin \alpha)$  
and $\quad \ddot{y} = -\omega^2(9e \sin 3\alpha + R \sin \alpha) + \dot{\omega}(3e \cos 3\alpha + R \cos \alpha)$ $\left.\right\}$ (A.33)

$\therefore \quad A = \{\omega^4[(9e)^2 + R^2 + 18eR \cos 2\alpha] + \dot{\omega}^2[(9e)^2 + R^2 + 6eR \cos 2\alpha]$
$\qquad - [12\dot{\omega}\omega^2 eR \sin 2\alpha]\}^{\frac{1}{2}}$ (A.34)

The direction of the acceleration is given by

$$\tan \beta = \frac{\ddot{y}}{\ddot{x}}$$

or $\beta = \arctan\left[\dfrac{\omega^2(9e \sin 3\alpha + R \sin \alpha) - \dot{\omega}(3e \cos 3\alpha + R \cos \alpha)}{\omega^2(9e \cos 3\alpha + R \cos \alpha) + \dot{\omega}(3e \sin 3\alpha + R \sin \alpha)}\right]$ (A.35)

It is, however, more relevant to determine the velocity and acceleration of the apex seals along and transverse to a radial vector so that the components along and transverse to the axis of the seal may be obtained by resolution.

Let $r$ be the radial distance of the tracing point or apex $D$ from the centre of the epitrochoid $0$. The equations of motion of the seals are then;

(a) Radial component of velocity, $U = \dot{r}$  
(b) Transverse component of velocity, $V = r\dot{\theta}$  
(c) Radial component of acceleration, $A_r = \ddot{r} - r(\dot{\theta})^2$  
(d) Transverse component of acceleration, $A_t = r\ddot{\theta} + 2\dot{r}\dot{\theta}$  $\left.\right\}$ (A.36)

From Equations A.2, $r = (e^2 + R^2 + 2eR \cos 2\alpha)^{\frac{1}{2}}$ $\qquad\qquad$ (A.37)

and $\tan \theta = \dfrac{(e \sin 3\alpha + R \sin \alpha)}{(e \cos 3\alpha + R \cos \alpha)}$ $\qquad\qquad$ (A.38)

Therefore,

(a) *The radial component of velocity*

$$U = \dot{r} = \omega \frac{dr}{d\alpha}$$

$$\therefore \quad U = \frac{-2eR\omega \sin 2\alpha}{(e^2 + R^2 + 2eR \cos 2\alpha)^{\frac{1}{2}}} \qquad\qquad \text{(A.39)}$$

(b) *The transverse component of velocity*

$$V = r\dot{\theta} = \omega r \frac{d\theta}{d\alpha}$$

Now $\dfrac{d}{d\alpha}(\tan \theta) = \dfrac{x\left(\dfrac{dy}{d\alpha}\right) - y\left(\dfrac{dx}{d\alpha}\right)}{x^2}$

i.e. $\sec^2 \theta . \dfrac{d\theta}{d\alpha} = \dfrac{xy' - yx'}{x^2}$

where $x' = \dfrac{dx}{d\alpha}$ and $y' = \dfrac{dy}{d\alpha}$

But $\sec^2 \theta = (1 + \tan^2 \theta) = \dfrac{x^2 + y^2}{x^2} = \dfrac{r^2}{x^2}$

Hence $\dfrac{d\theta}{d\alpha} = \dfrac{xy' - yx'}{r^2}$

or $\dfrac{d\theta}{d\alpha} = \dfrac{3e^2 + r^2 + 4eR \cos 2\alpha}{r^2}$ $\qquad\qquad$ (A.40)

$$\therefore \quad V = \omega . \frac{3e^2 + R^2 + 4eR \cos 2\alpha}{(e^2 + R^2 + 2eR \cos 2\alpha)^{\frac{1}{2}}} \qquad\qquad \text{(A.41)}$$

(c) *The radial component of acceleration*

$$A_r = \ddot{r} - r(\dot{\theta})^2$$

$$= \omega^2 \frac{d^2 r}{d\alpha^2} + \dot{\omega} \frac{dr}{d\alpha} - r\omega^2 \left(\frac{d\theta}{d\alpha}\right)^2$$

$$\therefore A_r = \frac{\omega^2(-r^2 4eR \cos 2\alpha - 4e^2 R^2 \sin^2 2\alpha)}{r^3} -$$

$$- \frac{\dot\omega 2eR \sin 2\alpha}{r} - \frac{\omega^2 r(3e^2 + R^2 + 4eR \cos 2\alpha)^2}{r^4}$$

$$\therefore A_r = -\omega^2 \left[ \frac{4eR \cos 2\alpha(3R^2 + 7e^2 + 5eR \cos 2\alpha) + (9e^2 + R^2)(e^2 + R^2)}{(e^2 + R^2 + 2eR \cos 2\alpha)^{3/2}} \right]$$

$$- \frac{\dot\omega 2eR \sin 2\alpha}{(e^2 + R^2 + 2eR \cos 2\alpha)^{\frac{1}{4}}} \tag{A.42}$$

(d) *The transverse component of acceleration*

$$A_t = r\ddot\theta + 2\dot r\dot\theta$$

$$= \omega^2 \frac{r\mathrm{d}^2\theta}{\mathrm{d}\alpha^2} + \dot\omega \frac{\mathrm{d}\theta}{\mathrm{d}\alpha} + 2\omega^2 \frac{\mathrm{d}\theta}{\mathrm{d}\alpha} \cdot \frac{\mathrm{d}r}{\mathrm{d}\alpha}$$

Hence $A_t = -\dfrac{\omega^2 8eR \sin 2\alpha + \dot\omega(3e^2 + R^2 + 4eR \cos 2\alpha)}{(e^2 + R^2 + 2eR \cos 2\alpha)^{\frac{1}{4}}}$ $\tag{A.43}$

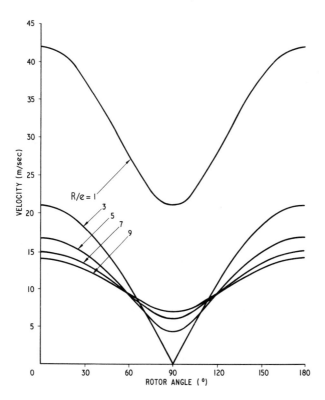

Fig. A10. *Apex velocity.* $R = 100\ mm$  $\dot\alpha = 1{,}000\ rev/min$

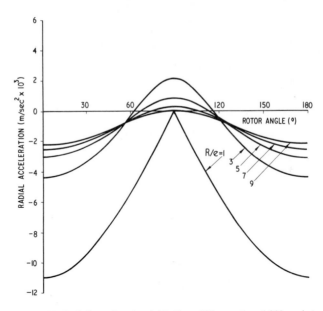

Fig. A11. Radial acceleration ($A_r$). $R = 100$ mm. $\dot{\alpha} = 1,000$ rev/min

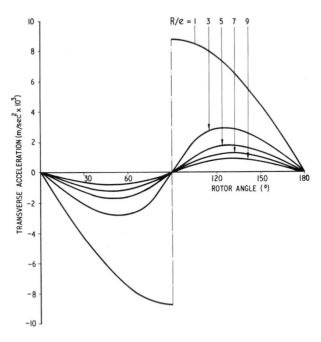

Fig. A12. Transverse acceleration ($A_t$). $R = 100$ mm, $\dot{\alpha} = 1,000$ rev/min

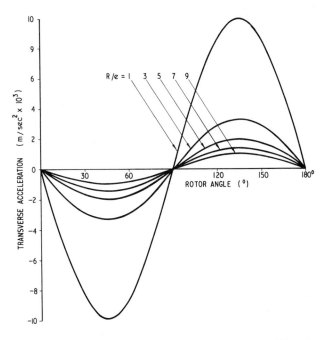

*Fig. A13. Transverse acceleration ($S_t$). R = 100 mm, $\dot{\alpha}$ = 1,000 rev/min*

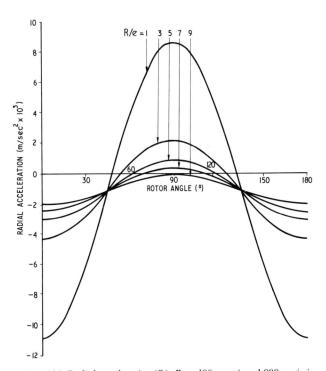

*Fig. A14. Radial acceleration ($S_r$). R = 100 mm, $\dot{\alpha}$ = 1,000 rev/min*

The radial and transverse accelerations of the apex may now be resolved along and transverse to the axis of the seal (the radius $O'D$) as follows.

Let $\gamma =$ Angle between $OD$ and $O'D$, then from Fig. A.8,

$$\frac{e}{\sin \gamma} = \frac{r}{\sin (\pi - 2\alpha)}$$

$\therefore \qquad \sin \gamma = \dfrac{e \sin 2\alpha}{(e^2 + R^2 + 2eR \cos 2\alpha)^{\frac{1}{2}}}$ \hfill (A.44)

and $\qquad \cos \gamma = \dfrac{(R^2 + e \cos 2\alpha(e \cos 2\alpha + 2R))^{\frac{1}{2}}}{(e^2 + R^2 + 2eR \cos 2\alpha)^{\frac{1}{2}}}$ \hfill (A.45)

Hence resolving along $O'D$

$$\left.\begin{array}{l} S_r = A_r \cos \gamma - A_t \sin \gamma \\ S_t = A_t \cos \gamma + A_r \sin \gamma \end{array}\right\}$$ \hfill (A.46)

Figs. A.10–14 show velocities and accelerations for a series of Wankel engines where $R = 100$ mm, the rotor speed is 1,000 rev/min and $R/e = 1, 3, 5, 7$ and 9. Rotor acceleration has been set to zero.

## A.8. Torque

The torque from the gas loads can be calculated with reference to Fig. A.15.

Let $p_{1, 2, 3,}$ indicate the gas pressures in each chamber respectively. Then the moment arm for the flank at pressure $p_1$ is given by $m_1 = e \sin 2\alpha$

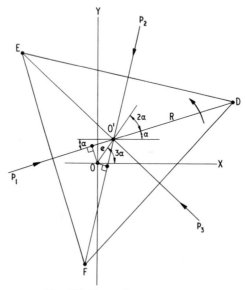

Fig. A15. Torque from gas pressures

for $p_2$, $m_2 = e \sin \left( \dfrac{\pi}{3} - 2\alpha \right)$

and for $p_3$, $m_3 = e \sin \left( \dfrac{2\pi}{3} - 2\alpha \right)$

or $m_3 = e \sin \left( \dfrac{\pi}{3} + 2\alpha \right)$ since $\sin (\pi - A) = + \sin A$.

Hence the torque is given by:

$$T(\alpha) = Ae \left[ p_1 \sin 2\alpha + p_2 \sin \left( \frac{\pi}{3} - 2\alpha \right) - p_3 \sin \left( \frac{\pi}{3} + 2\alpha \right) \right] \qquad (A.47)$$

where $A$ is the area of a flank.

The expression is cyclic with period $2\pi/3$ which can be seen by adding $2\pi/3$ to $\alpha$ to give the following expression:

$$T \left( \alpha + \frac{2\pi}{3} \right) = Ae \left[ -p_1 \sin \left( \frac{\pi}{3} + 2\alpha \right) + p_2 \sin 2\alpha + p_3 \sin \left( \frac{\pi}{3} - 2\alpha \right) \right]$$

The pressure $p_{1, 2, 3,}$ are identified with a particular face of the rotor.

## A.9. Circular Arc Approximation to Rotor Flank

The circular arc approximation to the rotor flank is obtained by considering the rotor at the t.d.c. or maximum compression position. The rotor flank is then assumed to touch the bore of the stator at three positions only. That is, at two adjacent apexes and at the minor axis of the epitrochoid. The third apex also contacts the epitrochoid at the opposite side of the minor axis as shown in Fig. A.16.

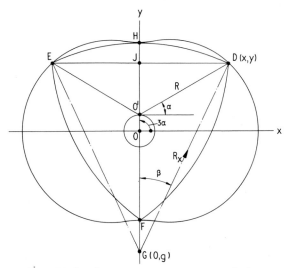

Fig. A16. Circular arc approximation to rotor flank

Let the centre of the rotor flank arc lie at $(O, g)$ in this position. Since $O'$ lies on the $y$-axis, $3\alpha = \pi/2$ or $\alpha = \pi/6$.

Hence in triangle $JGD$,

$$(R-e+g)^2 = \left(e+R\cos\frac{\pi}{3}+g\right)^2 + \left(R\sin\frac{\pi}{3}\right)^2$$

which leads to

$$g = \frac{eR\left(1+\cos\frac{\pi}{3}\right)}{R\left(1-\cos\frac{\pi}{3}\right)-2e} \tag{A.48}$$

The equivalent radius $R_x$ is then given by

$$R_x = R-e+g$$

$$R_x = R-e+\left[\frac{eR\left(1+\cos\frac{\pi}{3}\right)}{R\left(1-\cos\frac{\pi}{3}\right)-2e}\right]$$

Hence, $R_x = R-e+\dfrac{3eR}{(R-4e)}$ \tag{A.49}

The half angle $\beta$ subtended by the rotor flank is then given by

$$\beta = \arctan\left[\frac{R\sin\frac{\pi}{3}}{\left[\frac{eR\left(1+\cos\frac{\pi}{3}\right)}{R\left(1-\cos\frac{\pi}{3}\right)-2e}\right]+R\cos\left(\frac{\pi}{3}\right)+e}\right]$$

$$\text{or } \beta = \arctan\left[\frac{\frac{\sqrt{3}R}{2}}{\left[\frac{3eR}{R-4e}\right]+\frac{R}{2}+e}\right]$$

$$\beta = \arctan\left[\frac{\sqrt{3}R}{\left[\frac{6eR}{R-4e}\right]+R+2e}\right] \tag{A.50}$$

The arc length between adjacent apexes is then $2R_x \cdot \beta$ and, for example, in a typical engine where $R = 7$ cm and $e = 1$ cm, the arc length is 12·613 cm. The arc length of a rotor based on the inner envelope to the epitrochoid is 12·675 cm for an engine of the same dimensions. The difference in arc length is seen to be small, but the circular arc approximation should be used with considerable caution when calculating the surface/volume ratio. The following Table illustrates the surface/volume ratios for the circular arc approximation and the inner envelope rotors for an engine where $R = 7$ cm, $e = 1$ cm and $b = 1$ cm.

**Table A.1.** SURFACE TO VOLUME RATIO $(cm^2/cm^3)$

| Rotor Angle | Circular Arc | Inner Envelope |
|---|---|---|
| t.d.c. | 11.19506 | 14.17081 |
| 30° a.t.d.c. | 4.24254 | 4.38311 |
| 30° b.b.d.c. | 2.97008 | 2.99446 |
| b.d.c. | 2.78213 | 2.79742 |

The greatest discrepancy occurs at the important t.d.c. position where very minor changes in the rotor profile cause considerable changes in the compressed volume. The effect at the other positions is relatively minor and negligible at b.d.c.

## A.10. Calculation of the Surface/Volume Ratio

The calculation of the surface/volume ratio is straightforward in principle but because of the complexity of integrations involved, it is convenient to use a digital computer to evaluate the expressions.

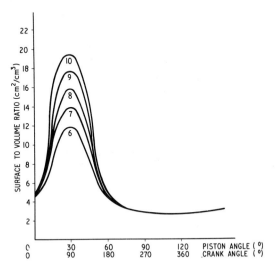

Fig. A17. Surface/volume ratio e = 1 cm, b = 1 cm, R/e = 6, 7, 8, 9, and 10

The calculation is carried out in a number of steps as follows:

1. The length of the inner envelope rotor flank between adjacent apexes is calculated from Equation A.15.
2. The length of the arc of the epitrochoid between adjacent rotor apexes is calculated from Equations A.2.
3. From these lengths, the surface area of a chamber is established using the expressions derived earlier for the area bounded by an epitrochoid and two adjacent apexes i.e., Equation A.23.
4. Finally, the surface/volume ratio is established using the expressions for chamber volume at a given crank angle, i.e. Equation A.23 × chamber width.

Fig. A.17 is a graph of the surface/volume ratio through a cycle for engines where $e = 1$ cm, $b = 1$ cm and $R$ ranges 6–10 cms.

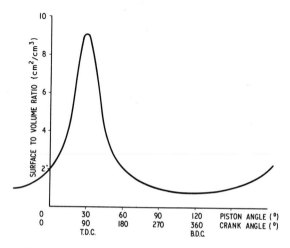

*Fig. A18. Spider engine K KM 502 R = 10 cm; e = 1·4 cm; b = 6·7 cm.
No allowance for flank depression*

Fig. A.18 shows the surface/volume ratio of the NSU KKM 502 Spider engine making no allowance for depressions in the rotor flanks or for the effects of the equidistant or parallel curve.

REFERENCES
1. DEAUX, R., *Introduction to the Geometry of Complex Numbers,* Unger Publishing Co., New York, (1957)
2. SYLVESTER, J. J., 'On the Plagiograph' *Nature,* **12,** 168, 214–6, (1875).

# Notation

$a$ = radius of generating circle
$b$ = radius of base circle
$c$ = normal distance between epitrochoidal path and parallel curve
$e$ = eccentricity = centre distance of phasing gears
$f$ = distance from apex to instantaneous centre
$h$ = distance from rotor centre to instantaneous centre
$r$ = polar radius of apex
$u, v$ = defined in Section on envelopes
$v$ = velocity along epitrochoid
$A, A_{r, t}$ = absolute, radial and transverse accelerations, respectively
$C$ = area between adjacent apexes and chord joining those apexes
$0, 0'$ = co-ordinate system and rotor centres respectively
$R$ = generating radius
$S_{r, t}$ = acceleration components along and transverse to generating radius of rotor
$U, V$ = radial and transverse velocities, respectively
$Z$ = number of apexes on rotor
$\alpha$ = rotor angle
$\gamma$ = angle between generating radius and polar radius
$\theta$ = polar angle of apex
$\phi$ = crank angle
$\omega$ = angular velocity of rotor = $d\alpha/dt$
$\dot{\omega}$ = angular acceleration of rotor = $d^2\alpha/dt^2$
Differentiation with respect to $\alpha$ shown by dash i.e. $x' = dx/d\alpha$

# Index